RESOLVING PATIENT AMBIVALENCE

A Five Session Motivational Interviewing Intervention

Developed by

Ann Fields, MA, CADC III, CGAC II
Portland, Oregon
2006

A MODEL FOR BROAD APPLICATION

THIS MOTIVATIONAL INTERVIEWING INTERVENTION HAS BROAD APPLICATION FOR ALL HEALTH PROVIDERS, MEDICAL SOCIAL WORKERS, EDUCATORS AND OTHER HUMAN SERVICE PRACTITIONERS.

IT ALLOWS FOR THE FACILITATION AND IMPLEMENTATION OF MOTIVATIONAL INTERVIEWING STRATEGIES WITHIN **FIVE GROUP SESSIONS**.

THIS GROUP PROCESS AND APPROACH ELICITS AND EFFECTS POSITIVE CHANGE IN THE LIVES OF PEOPLE STRUGGLING WITH LIFE CHOICES AND PERSONAL BEHAVIORS, AFFECTING THEIR OVERALL HEALTH, WELLBEING AND FUNCTIONING.

*Note – Throughout this manual "changing your problem health behavior" can be any problem health behavior / lifestyle change (e.g. substance abuse, smoking, eating disorders, fluid intake, diet changes, stress, exercise, taking medications, and managing other health concerns).

Table of Contents

Acknowledgements

I would like to thank my partner, Mindy Holliday, Program Director / Assistant Professor of the Child Welfare Partnership in the Graduate School of Social Work, at Portland State University, for her ongoing encouragement, inspiration and business ingenuity in assisting me in completing this project. I would also like to thank Nikki Johnson, Director of Daystar Education Associates and Adjunct Faculty at Portland Community College, for her openness as a teacher, her generosity in time and commitment in completing this project and her professional integrity as a trainer, writer and mentor. Both Mindy and Nikki assisted me in taking my vision of this project and making it into a reality. I would also like to thank my family (Jenni, Michael, Robbie, Sarah, Jen, John, Andy, Erin, Allie, John and Stephanie) for their love and support.

Ann Fields
June, 2006

This document represents Ann Fields' move from practitioner to information disseminator. Ann has used and refined this model through her years of clinical practice. She has trained various groups in the theory and practice of motivational interviewing. In this endeavor she presents in a concrete and explicit way, the structure she uses in her groups.

This document is designed to be a manual for practitioners, with all of the details provided, including the paperwork and logistical tips she has learned through trial and error. It will be most successfully utilized in the context of being trained with the model and receiving this manual as part of the training. We are not naïve enough to think that will always happen. So it is very complete. People with some training and appreciation for motivational interviewing will also readily apply it. But Ann has painstakingly provided the conceptual models for every action taken. People with little background in MI will learn and *experience* MI if they take the direction provided here.

It has been my pleasure to help Ann put this on paper in a form designed to help train others. For my experience in this project, I saw the articulateness and thoughtfulness that went into each element of the group. Every action was calculated in service to the enhancement of patient motivation. Ann has done her homework. Practitioners will benefit and patients will benefit from her contributions to helping people with problem health behaviors change.

Finally, this manual, with its use of motivational interviewing, gets providers back to the basics. This model requires that providers once again, listen and listen deeply to their patients and use what they hear to motivate change. It is patient centered, but it is certainly not non-directive.

Nikki Johnson, MA
Daystar Education Associates

Why Design a Motivational Group?

I took William Miller's first training for trainers in 1993. When I began to utilize a motivational style and motivational strategies with my individual clients, I saw how effecting change was a process. It became clear to me that Motivational Interviewing (MI) could be utilized in a variety of settings with diverse populations and with diverse needs. I explored research-based conceptual models for understanding motivation and developed exercises to be facilitated with an MI approach. I found these exercises to be revealing, eliciting problem recognition, discrepancies, change talk and affecting an individual's process of change.

In 1996 I was working in a gambling addiction agency where clients had weekly individual counseling. As the political climate changed and the budgets cuts greater, group counseling became the primary modality available. It was during this time that I started to explore how I could utilize motivational interviewing strategies in a group format. The research stated MI improved treatment retention by decreasing resistance and enhancing client motivation and commitment for change. I selected the exercises I had designed from the conceptual models for understanding motivation that would effect client movement in the earlier stages of change. I began formulating the rationale for the group, its purpose, and a description of the mindset needed to facilitate a motivational group. What resulted was a five-week group, with sessions lasting one and a half hours, once per week. This was an open group, where new members could join at any time. The group was utilized for individuals at various stages of change. The group consisted of 1) clients at the beginning of their treatment, who were not ready for change, and for 2) clients in the middle of their treatment, who started out in action, but were showing signs of ambivalence and 3) for clients at the end of their treatment for closure and recommitment to their goals. It became a very powerful group, eliciting and increasing an individual's commitment and confidence levels to change their problem behavior.

During my years of implementing and training motivational interviewing and this group model, I found this group model to be applicable across a variety of practice venues, which included both client and patient populations. Most people have the internal resources to make changes, but lack the commitment and/or confidence levels to make the decision to change. This five-session group model helps resolve ambivalence and increases an individual's intrinsic desire for change.

Conceptual Models For Understanding Motivation: A Review

How I utilized conceptual models for understanding motivation in my curriculum with patient populations in mind.

1. **Stages of Change** – Prochaska & DiClemente's process of change (1991) defined several stages through which people <u>normally</u> pass in the process of changing.

Both providers and patients need to be educated regarding the stages of change. Providers need to understand the change process to: 1) normalize where patients are in the process of change and 2) to utilize appropriate strategies to assist patients in moving through the different stages. Patients need to understand the change process to normalize what they may experience related to changing a particular problem health behavior.

CURRICULUM:
- ***Session One – Orientation / Pre – Assessment Exercises:*** *The provider will educate new patients on the Stages of Change. Patients assess where they are on the change wheel.*
- ***Session Five – Vision / Post – Assessment Exercises:*** *The Stages of Change are utilized with patients as a **Post** – self-assessment exercise to compare with their **Pre**-self-assessment exercise they completed in Session One. During this time patients are able to identify their movement in the change process, as forward, backward, or the same.*

2. **Conflict – ambivalence** – In conflict situations, ambivalence is a normal, defining condition of the stage of contemplation, and is a key obstacle to change.

Both providers and patients need to understand that feeling two ways about changing a problem health behavior is normal. It is up to providers to assist patients in clarifying and resolving their ambivalence through the use of appropriate strategies. Ambivalence is not resistance.

CURRICULUM:
- ***Session One - Orientation:*** *The provider will normalize ambivalence when he/she is educating patients about the stage of contemplation in the wheel of change.*
- ***Session Three - Pros & Cons:*** *The provider will also facilitate patients in weighing both sides of their ambivalence, related to the costs and benefits of their problem health behavior.*

3. **Health Beliefs Model** – Ronald Rogers Protection Theory (1976) states motivation for change depends upon the presence of a sufficient degree of perceived risks, in combination with sufficient self-efficacy.

Both providers and patients need to understand that for change to occur, patients need to: 1) become aware of the possibility of risks and/or the severity of risks, if they continue to engage in a particular problem health behavior and 2) their degree of self-efficacy. If patients have low self-efficacy, their belief that change is possible will be low. Providers need to utilize appropriate strategies to increase patient's awareness of risks and assess patient's degree of self-efficacy, for change to occur.

CURRICULUM:
- *Session One – Orientation / Pre-Assessment Exercises: The provider educates patients about the importance of becoming aware of risks and self-efficacy, when discussing the process of moving from contemplation to preparation in the Stages of Change. The provider also provides patients with two self- assessment exercises to raise their awareness of risks and rate their degree of self-efficacy: 1) **Areas of Impact** – To assess the degree of impact their particular problem health behavior has had on the different areas of their lives. 2) **Commitment / Confidence Rating** – To rate their commitment level to change their problem health behavior and rate their confidence level, that they have the skills to change their problem health behavior.*
- *Session Two – Feelings Exercise 2: Patients become aware of their feelings related to the different areas of their lives that have been impacted by their problem health behavior.*
- *Session Three – Pros & Cons Exercise: Patients become aware of the pros and cons of their problem health behavior. Patients identify and clarify their short-term pros. The provider assists patients in identifying and clarifying ways they have successfully avoided and/or altered their short-term pros. The provider also addresses patient's degree of self-efficacy by affirming and reflecting what has worked and by providing additional options and choices.*

4. **Decisional Balance** – Janis & Mann (1977). Decision is a process of weighing the pros & cons of change cognitively.

Providers need to assist their patients in weighing out the short and long term pros and cons of continuing their problem health behavior. This helps patients clarify and assess their need for change. They weigh the different factors that do or do not support their problem health behavior. With the use of appropriate MI strategies, this problem-solving skill can allow for decision-making that leans toward change, based on patient's own arguments for change.

CURRICULUM:
- *Session Three – Pros & Cons: The provider will ask the group to brainstorm the short and long-term pros and cons of continuing their problem health behavior.*

5. **Reactance** – Brehm Theory (1981). When behavioral freedom and autonomy are threatened, the probability and perceived desirability of the to-be-lost behavior will increase.

Both providers and patients need to understand that reactance is normal. Providers need to expect and normalize feelings of reactance, especially when patients have been required or pressured to make a change. Providers facilitate patients in expressing and clarifying those

feelings of reactance. This process allows patients to take back ownership and responsibility for their own choices and decisions related to change.

CURRICULUM:
- **Session One – Orientation / Pre-Assessment Exercises:** *The provider will educate new patients about reactance, and normalize their feelings related to being required to change their problem health behavior. The provider will have patients complete the* **Freedom Exercise,** *and have patients read out loud what they have written.*
- **Session Two – Feelings Exercise 1:** *Patients will identify and describe their feelings related to being required or pressured to change.*

6. <u>Self-Perception Theory</u> – D. J. Bem (1972). When people publicly take a position, their commitment to that position increases.
   *It is the patient who should present the argument for change.

Providers need to utilize MI strategies throughout the group process. Providers will listen, reflect and affirm change talk. The exercises are designed to elicit change talk. Patients reading out loud what they write solidify their own arguments for change.

CURRICULUM:

All exercises are designed to evoke change talk: problem recognition, areas of concern, intentions to change and optimism about the possibility of change. Patients read all completed exercises out loud. This process increases patient's commitments to making change. The provider also reflects and affirms the patient's commitments. Patients may hear their change talk again by listening to other patients who may give voice to similar reasons for change.

7. <u>Self-Regulation Theory</u> – F.H. Kanfer (1986). To trigger change, one would seek to increase the discrepancy between current status and goal. **"Where I see myself going & where I want to be."**

Providers will utilize the exercises to increase patient's awareness of the discrepancies between current status and goal. Both the values clarification exercise and vision exercise increase patient's awareness of the discrepancies between status and goal and trigger intrinsic desires for change.

CURRICULUM:
- **Session Four – Values Exercise 1:** *Patients will identify, prioritize and define their top six values. Patients are then asked to describe how their problem health behavior impacts each of their values and/or which of their values support their problem health behavior. The provider allows patients to experience the feeling of discomfort related to the discrepancy between their problem health behavior and values.*
- **Session Five – Vision / Post-Assessment Exercises:** *Patients present their vision of possible changes and improvements in various areas of their lives that were impacted by their problem health behavior. They will describe their feeling and values related to those changes.*

8. **Value Theory** – M. Rokeach (1979). The Nature of Human Values. Rokeach conceptualized personality as hierarchically organized:

Immediate Behavior & Cognitions
Individual Attitudes
Beliefs
Core Values
Sense of
Personal
Identity

"The further 'in' the shift occurs, the more sweeping will be the resulting change."

CURRICULUM:
- *Session Four – Values Exercise 1: Patients will identify, prioritize and define their top six values. Patients are then asked to describe how their problem health behavior impacts each of their values and/or which of their values support their problem health behavior. The provider allows patients to experience the feeling of discomfort related to the discrepancy between their problem health behavior and values.*

- *Exercise Four – Values Exercise2 (Homework): Patients are asked to keep their values in mind for one week and describe the behaviors and/or activities that they engaged in that support each of their values. **This exercise allows patients to experience how it feels to decrease the discrepancy between their problem health behavior and values.***

If we understand these conceptual models we have a framework for facilitating motivation and effecting change. William Miller's research showed that a therapist can significantly influence client motivation. "Motivation is not seen as a patient trait but the interpersonal process between provider and patient." "How a provider thinks about motivation and change greatly influences what a provider does."

I have been inspired and motivated with the results of this process. It returns us to the basics of patient centeredness where respect and positive regard of each individual is paramount. MI provides a structure that gives responsibility back to the patient for change, relieving providers of that assumed "burden." Once patients have made a commitment for change, providers can more successfully provide support and strategies to assist patients in achieving their goals.

Curriculum Outline
For Each Session

OPEN GROUP FORMAT

The Orientation (session one) must be held at a separate time from the motivation group (sessions two-five). All new members must complete the Orientation (session one), before starting the motivation group (sessions two-five). This format allows the motivation group to remain open for new members. Depending on patient flow, having an Orientation Session scheduled every week may be necessary.

The patient's final session is their presentations of "the vision" they have completed as homework. If patients come for their final session without completing it, they should complete it while the rest of the group is working on a different exercise and present it at the end of group. They will stay after group to complete their post assessment exercises and review them with the facilitator.

SESSION ONE: Orientation
Time Allowed: One hour

Rationale
Based on Daryl Bem's Self-Perception Theory (1972), people learn what they believe in the same way others do, by hearing themselves talk. Facilitating a motivational group allows this process to occur. At orientation, the facilitator starts the process through the use of self-assessment exercises, inherent in the process is the expectation that patients will read what they have written out loud. When people publicly take a position, their commitment to that position increases. It is the patients who should present their arguments for change. Let patients confront their own arguments for change. Allow for discrepancies to build. To confront means to bring together for close examination.

Purpose of this session
The purpose of this session is to prepare the patient for the MI group. To do so, the patient is informed about group norms, which include: group ethics, self-assessment exercises and the schedule for group attendance. The patient is provided an overview of the process they will go through, timeline, materials used, and how materials will be kept from week to week. During this session, the patient's baseline level of motivation and confidence will be measured. The patient will be oriented to the MI philosophy and become clear about what their next step in treatment will be.

Facilitator Mind Set
Facilitators engage patients by utilizing an empathetic style of reflective listening, accurate understanding, acceptance and respect. Roll with resistance. Trust the process (don't need to push it). The exercises elicit change talk. Listen for and affirm change talk. Let patients hear themselves. Know when to be quiet. Don't debate, argue or confront.

Materials needed for this session
Supplies: folders, pens, clipboards, dry erase board and dry erase pen.

Patient Handouts
    Group Norms
    Facilitator philosophy
    Freedom handout
    Purpose of the group

Areas of Impact
Stages of Change
Self-Commitment Rating
Treatment Plan
Group Summary

Other Paperwork
Patient Sign In sheet
Roster/tracking sheet

Procedures

1.   Set up chairs in a circle. Have all chairs the same.

2.   Put facilitator name, name of group and the next day and time of group on the board.

3.   Have patients sign-in and as the facilitator checks the roster, (Sign-In Handout and Roster are located at the back of this manual, under Forms).

4.   Introduce self and the Orientation session by saying, "I will review with you the group norms, expectations and group process. I will also have you complete some self assessment exercises."

5.   Have patients briefly introduce themselves: their name, why they are in group, who their provider is and if they are attending any other groups.

6.   Review **Handout 1- Group Norms (p.19)**. The facilitator will review each item on the ethics section, focusing on safety and honesty. Emphasize that honesty plays an important role in this group. Patients will be given an exercise to complete each time they come to group. The more honest patients are in completing their exercises, the more they will gain from the exercises.

7.   Distribute a folder to each participant. Have them put their name on it. Explain that you will make copies of the completed exercises at the end of each group, but patients will keep the originals in their folder. The facilitator will offer to keep patient's folders week to week or patients can choose to take their folders with them, as long as them bring them to group each week.

8. Continue on with the handout, emphasizing attendance policy. Emphasize the importance of attending each group, over the next four weeks, so they can benefit from the accumulative effect of the exercises.

9. The facilitator will explain the group process. Even though patients will be in a group setting, they will be doing their own individual work. No cross talk or debating what people say or write is allowed. This provides safety, so patients can speak freely and write what is on their mind. Everyone will complete the exercise and then read it out loud. Spelling and grammar don't matter. They will benefit from hearing themselves read out-loud, what they have written. Explain, that at times, is it is like a one room schoolhouse, where people will be working on different exercises during the same group session.

    Highlight the basic process for each week:
    *   Sign in
    *   Check in (5 minutes total)
    *   Reflect on Change (Quote)
    *   Homework Review
    *   Explain the group exercise.
    *   Participants do the exercise.
    *   Participants will read their exercises out loud
    *   Participants will fill out the group summary, while facilitator makes copies of the exercises.
    *   Hand back originals for patients to put into their folders. Collect group summaries. Collect folders.

10. Review **Handout 2 – Philosophy (p.20).** The facilitator talks about self and philosophy of working with people. Emphasize experience in various settings. Labeling does not work. Express desire to get to know who each of them is.

11. The facilitator discusses feelings related to being required or pressured to make changes. Brehm's (1981) Reactance Theory states, that perceived threats to personal freedom and choice will elicit behaviors designed to demonstrate and restore that freedom. When behavioral freedom and autonomy are threatened, the probability and perceived desirability of the to-be-lost behavior will increase. It is normal to feel resistant when independence and freedom of choice have been taken away. Recognize that most people make changes on their own. The purpose of this group

process is for the patient to decide what if anything they want to do regarding changing their problem health behavior. Even if their health care provider or loved one is requiring or pressuring them to make changes, the decision to make changes is always the patient's choice.

12.   Review **Handout 3 – Freedom Exercise (p.22)**. "Spend the next five minutes answering the four questions." Group members will read all their answers on the page, before facilitator goes to the next person. For each person, on question four, where they rate their level of freedom, whatever number they circled, ask why it is not lower on the scale. Also ask what they would have to do to make it higher on the scale.

13.   Distribute **Handout 4 – Purpose of Group (p.23).** Read it out loud to group. Ask them what they related to. If people are unsure on what they need to do, it will help them come to a decision. If they have made a decision, it will help them clarify and recommit to it. Explain that having a medical problem may cause people to lose a sense of who they are and where they are going. This group gives them the opportunity to focus on themselves and what if anything they want to do, regarding changing their problem health behavior.

14.   Distribute **Handout 5 – Areas of Impact (p. 25)**. Have them complete Part A first. When everyone is done, explain Part B. This is introduced with the phrase "Select from the list above the items you have circled 3 or 4. List those areas in order of importance." When everyone is finished, have them each read Part B (their prioritized list) out loud.

Facilitator Hint: If they say they don't have any 3's or 4's, have them prioritize their twos. If they have all ones, don't worry about it (roll with resistance).

15.   Review and discuss **Handout Wheel of Change (p.27).** This exercise is based on Prochaska and DiClemente's process of change, which defines several stages that people normally pass through in the process of changing their behavior. The facilitator explains "I want you to understand how people change. It has been studied a lot, and recently studied how people struggling with problem health behaviors change. The researchers realized people change in similar ways, they go through stages".

Draw the wheel and write the stages of change on the board. Educate patients on the wheel of change by describing each stage. Use an example that is not a hot topic.

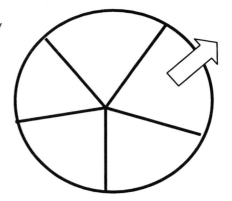

Example:

I have a car that keeps breaking down. My friends are giving me rides. My friends say, 'You need to get a new car'. I say, 'No I don't.'

This is Precontemplation. "I am hearing some concerns regarding my car, but I don't think I have a problem." This is an indication that this person has not entered the wheel.

Example:

Let's say my friends quit giving me rides. As a result I am late to work. My boss is upset with me. My kids aren't getting to their activities. And it is causing a safety issue, late on the road at night. I'm becoming aware of risks.

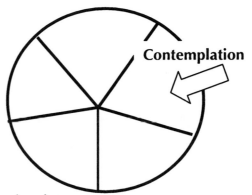

Once awareness of risks begins, people enter the wheel.

The first stage is Contemplation. In this stage people consider the possibility of change and at the same time, reject it. The primary feeling is ambivalence. In conflict situations, ambivalence is normal and is a critical obstacle to change. A person feels two ways about change. On one hand they think about the need for change. On the other hand, they reject it.

Example of ambivalence:

If my friends tell me the reasons I should get a new car, I will tell them all the reasons why I can't get a new car. And if they tell me why I shouldn't get another car, I will tell them all the reasons I should.

For a more serious problem, this is a painful place to be stuck.
(Ex. "These are the reasons I need to leave this relationship, and these are the reasons I don't").

     15

People can become immobilized when feelings of ambivalence are left unresolved. Also in past treatment experiences, providers or other people in authority may not have been aware of ambivalence as a normal stage of change and may have labeled patients as resistant or noncompliant.

Becoming aware of risks is not enough for change to occur. This is based on Ronald Rogers' Protection Motivation Theory, a health beliefs model. Motivation for change depends on the presence of a sufficient degree of perceived risk, in combination with sufficient self-efficacy. You need two things for change, awareness of risks and self-efficacy, the belief that change is possible.

Returning to my example of getting a new car:

> **Example:** *I don't know what to look for under the hood of a car, to make sure I'm getting a good one. I don't know how to talk to a car salesman, or go to the bank for a loan.*

If one doesn't know how to do these things, their self- efficacy is low. This means their belief that change is possible is low.

> **Example:** *Now, let's say I tell a friend and my friend says, I know someone who is great with cars, give him a call. I make an appointment and I feel a little bit of hope.*

When this occurs, they move into Preparation stage – They are leaning toward the possibility of change. This stage provides a small window of opportunity. It can close as quickly as it opens.

> **Example:** *Let's say my friend's friend doesn't show for the appointment to meet with me. How do I feel? Where might I go in the wheel? On the other hand, let's say he does show up and takes me to ten car lots and tells me what to look for under the hood of a car, and how to talk to a salesman and talk to a loan officer at a bank. Now I begin to feel hopeful and I think I can make the change with some additional help.*

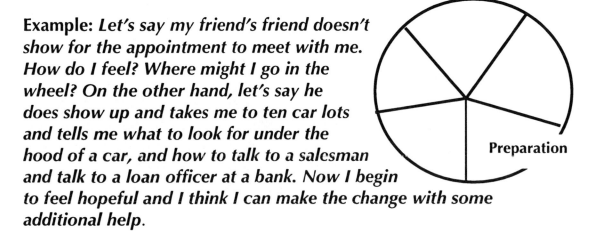

Preparation

As one's self-efficacy increases, they move from Preparation into Action. Most treatment facilities are *action* models. That means the minute a patient walks through the door providers expect them to be at the action stage. But what if they are in *Pre-contemplation or Contemplation*? If they come to treatment in Pre-contemplation and/or Contemplation, they need to learn about risks, resolve their ambivalence and increase their self-efficacy. In Action they have made up their mind to change. They want to make a change, it's their goal. If they are in Action, providers can teach them the strategies to make the change.

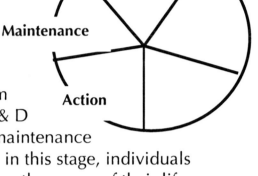

> *(Ex. I've already made my mind up to get a car; just teach me what I need to know to accomplish my goal).*

Once patients have made changes in their problem health behavior, they enter Maintenance. In the A& D treatment community, patients are considered in maintenance when they have abstained for 6-12 months. While in this stage, individuals have achieved their initial goal and are working on other areas pf their life impacted by their problem health behavior. This helps maintain their goal and keep their life moving forward.

Returning to my example*:*

> *Once I bought the car, I began to take care of other areas of my life. (e.g. making up time at work, and getting my kids back into their activities).*

Most people don't change from point A to point B in a linear fashion. Change is a process. It is more like an upward spiral than a line. For example, most people who quit smoking try many times, before they finally quit. Each time leads them closer to their goal. In the next stage notice that Relapse, is in the wheel, as a normal part of the change process.

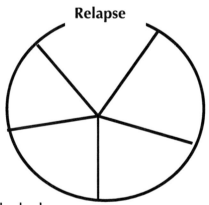

In the treatment community, relapse sometimes isn't handled well. It is not uncommon for patients to be labeled, reprimanded or discouraged from continuing treatment due to a relapse. After a relapse, people often experience a sense of hopelessness and despair and may give up on their goal. These internal attributions can be altered, by educating patients about relapse.

Providers can say:

Relapse is normal. It is about returning to old patterns and behaviors in vulnerable times and situations. At those times and in those situations you weren't prepared to handle them differently. If you acknowledge your relapse and stay in the wheel, and keep your goal in mind, you can move through the stages. In Action and Maintenance, you can learn strategies to strengthen those vulnerable areas and situations to prevent relapse from happening again. You need strategies to learn how to handle things differently.

16. **Handout 6- Wheel of Change (p.27)** Ask everyone to shade in where they think they are on the wheel as of today. One can be a sliver of one stage and much of another. Acknowledge that change is a process. Where ever one is, is ok. Ask everyone to read or show where they are on the wheel.

17. **Handout 7 Commitment Rating & Confidence Rating (p.29).** Have them rate their commitment level to accomplishing their goal, however they define it. Also have them rate their confidence level, how confident they feel that they have the skills to accomplish their goal. Group members read both ratings out loud.

18. Have patients hand in 4 exercises, (Handouts 3, 5, 6, & 7) making sure their names and the date is on them.

19. Have them read and sign the **Treatment Plans – Handout 8 (pg. 31),** that the facilitator prepared while they were doing the exercises. In addition, have them complete the **Handout - Group Summary (p. 32).** Ask patients not to leave as you go make copies of their exercises.

20. Return their original exercises back to patients to put in their folders. Collect from patients their Group Summaries and Treatment Plans.

21. Remind them of the meeting time next week. Thank them for their work.

Group Norms

Group Ethics
Safety
Respect
Confidentiality
Honesty

Group Materials
Folder
Exercises

Group Time
1 x a week, for 4 weeks

Missed Appointments
Notify provider in advance

Where do I go after completing motivation group?

Group process
Be in group on time.
Fill out Sign-in form
Identify patients who completed vision homework
Identify patients who will be receiving vision homework
Spend 5 minutes with group for check-in process
Review quote
Review completed homework
Provider explains exercises
Patients do identified exercise
Patients present their exercises in group
Review homework
5 minute check-out process

Facilitator's Philosophy

Labels:

I'm not going to label you (e.g. non-compliant or resistance), because ambivalence is normal. Also, if I had cancer; I would not like to be known as the "cancer patient". Cancer may impact different areas of my life, but it is not who I am. My name is Ann Fields... that is who I am...and in this group I am interested in getting to know who you are and what is important to each one of you at this time in your life.

Required to Change:

All of you have been required or pressured to change due to concerns regarding a problem health behavior, past and/or present. Some of these concerns may not necessarily be your own.

When you are required or pressured to change due to a health problem, your sense of decision-making, independence and choices may feel like they are not your own. You may feel confused, fearful and frustrated; even angry, like your world has been turned upside down. When your choices and decisions don't feel like your own, reactance is normal. In this group we will discuss your feelings related to being required or pressured to make a change and explore what, if anything, you may want to do about making changes in your life.

Name: *John*   Date: _____

FREEDOM

1. Describe your loss of freedom of choice, independence and decision-making once you entered the Medical System.

    I was told my diagnosis and prognosis and the changes I needed to make to improve my situation without involving me in the decision-making process. I was treated like a child.

2. What do you hope for and expect regarding your freedom of choice, independence and decision-making once you are no longer involved in the Medical System?

    My life back.

3. What disappoints you now, regarding your freedom of choice, independence and decision-making?

    I'm still not dealing with all the changes I need to make in my lifestyle, even though I've been told what the risks are if I don't change.

4. On a 1-10 scale, with 1 being no freedom and 10 being completely free, rate your sense of freedom of choice, independence and decision-making as of today?

    No freedom   Totally free

    0-------1-------2-------3-------④-------5-------6-------7-------8-------9-------10

Name: _____   Date:_____

FREEDOM

1. Describe your loss of freedom of choice, independence and decision-making once you entered the Medical System.

2. What do you hope for and expect regarding your freedom of choice, independence and decision-making once you are no longer involved in the Medical System?

3. What disappoints you now, regarding your freedom of choice, independence and decision-making?

4. On a 1-10 scale, with 1 being no freedom and 10 being completely free, rate your sense of freedom of choice, independence and decision-making as of today?

No freedom   Totally free

0-------1-------2-------3-------4-------5-------6-------7-------8-------9-------10

Purpose of Group

This group is to help you gain back some control over your own choices and decisions about this time in your life, by giving you a chance to reevaluate your life, and what you may want to do about the concerns related to your problem health behavior (e.g. smoking, substance use, taking your medications, etc.). What you do with this information is up to you. The final choice and decisions about any changes you make in your lives is always your own.

Re Evaluation Process—When feelings of confusion, anger and fear appear, in response to the need for a change in your life; compounded with feelings of not knowing who you are anymore and the direction your life is going, it is difficult to know where to begin. Not knowing where to begin is very common and some of the universal questions people start asking are:

Who Am I?
Where Am I Going?
What Is My Purpose?
How Do I Get There?

The first step to help you find some answers to these questions is to go through this group.

Pre-Assessment Exercise

Name: *John*   Date:_____

Areas of Impact Assessment

(Part A) On a scale of 1 - 4, with 1 being the **least** impacted, and 4 being the **most**, please circle the level of impact your problem health behavior has had on the different areas of your life.

Relationships	1	2	③	4
Work	1	②	3	4
Financial	1	②	3	4
Legal	1	②	3	4
Family	①	2	3	4
Education	1	②	3	4
Community	1	②	3	4
Physical Health	1	②	3	4
Emotional Health	1	2	③	4
Spirituality	①	2	3	4
Hobbies/Interests	1	2	③	4
Social Life	1	2	③	4
Character/Morals/Values	1	2	③	4
Self-esteem	1	②	3	4

(Part B) List the areas **most** impacted (3 or 4) by your problem health behavior, in order of importance.

1. *relationships*

2. *character, morals, values*

3. *emotional health*

4. *hobbies, interests*

5. *social life*

6.

7.

Pre-Assessment Exercise

Name: _____   Date:_____

Areas of Impact Assessment
(Part A) On a scale of 1 - 4, with 1 being the *least* impacted, and 4 being the *most,* please circle the level of impact your problem health behavior has had on the different areas of your life.

Relationships	1	2	3	4
Work	1	2	3	4
Financial	1	2	3	4
Legal	1	2	3	4
Family	1	2	3	4
Education	1	2	3	4
Community	1	2	3	4
Physical Health	1	2	3	4
Emotional Health	1	2	3	4
Spirituality	1	2	3	4
Hobbies/Interests	1	2	3	4
Social Life	1	2	3	4
Character/Morals/Values	1	2	3	4
Self-esteem	1	2	3	4

(Part B) List the areas *most* impacted (3 or 4) by your problem health behavior, in order of importance.

1.

2.

3.

4.

5.

6.

7.

8.

Pre-Assessment Exercise

Name: *John*   Date: _____

PROCHASKA-DICLEMENTE'S WHEEL OF CHANGE

Please read the definition of each stage of change, written below, and shade in the area of the wheel that identifies where you are, in the process of changing your problem health behavior.

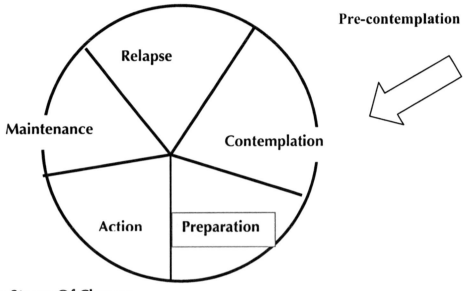

The Six Stages Of Change:

1. Pre-contemplation-**You do not think that your problem health behavior is a problem.**

2. Contemplation-**You are considering the possibility of changing your problem health behavior and at the same time rejecting the idea of change.**

3. Preparation-**You are leaning toward change, seriously considering no longer engaging in your problem health behavior.**

4. Action-**You are taking steps to no longer engage in your problem health behavior.**

5. Maintenance-**You are identifying and using strategies to prevent relapse and addressing other areas of your life.**

6. Relapse-**You are renewing the processes of contemplation, preparation and action and not giving up on your goal.**

Pre-Assessment Exercise

Name:_____   Date: _____

PROCHASKA-DICLEMENTE'S WHEEL OF CHANGE

Please read the definition of each stage of change, written below, and shade in the area of the wheel that identifies where you are, in the process of changing your problem health behavior.

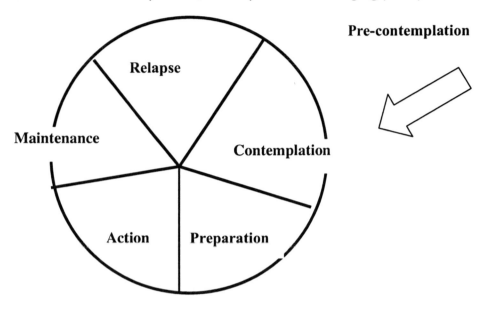

The Six Stages Of Change:

1. Pre-contemplation-**You do not think that your problem health behavior is a problem.**

2. Contemplation-**You are considering the possibility of changing your problem health behavior and at the same time rejecting the idea of change.**

3. Preparation-**You are leaning toward change, seriously considering no longer engaging in your problem health behavior.**

4. Action-**You are taking steps to no longer engage in your problem health behavior.**

5. Maintenance-**You are identifying and using strategies to prevent relapse and addressing other areas of your life.**

6. Relapse-**You are renewing the processes of contemplation, preparation and action and not giving up on your goal.**

Pre-Assessment Exercise

Name: *John*   Date: _____

Self-Commitment Rating

At this moment, how important is it that you change your problem health behavior? How hard are you willing to work and how much are you willing to do, to achieve this goal? Answer this question by writing a number from 0-100 in the designated space below, using the following scale as a guide.

1	25	50	75	100
Not important at all	Less important than most other things I would like to achieve	About as important as most of the other things I would like to achieve	More important than most of the other things I would like to achieve	The most important thing in my life

Write your goal importance rating (from 0-100) here: **65%** _____

Self-Confidence Rating (Do I believe I can succeed?)

In the designated space below indicate how confident you feel that you have the skills to achieve your stated goal?. Use the following scale as a guide.

0%	50%	100%
Not at all confident that I will achieve my goal	50-50 chance I will achieve my goal	Totally Confident I will Achieve my goal.

Write your confidence rating (from 0% - 100%) here: **100%** _____

Pre-Assessment Exercise

Name: _____   Date: _____

Self-Commitment Rating

At this moment, how important is it that you change your problem health behavior? How hard are you willing to work and how much are you willing to do, to achieve this goal? Answer this question by writing a number from 0-100 in the designated space below, using the following scale as a guide.

1	25	50	75	100
Not important at all	Less important than most other things I would like to achieve	About as important as most of the other things I would like to achieve	More important than most of the other things I would like to achieve	The most important thing in my life

Write your goal importance rating (from 0-100) here: _____

Self-Confidence Rating (Do I believe I can succeed?)

In the designated space below indicate how confident you feel that you have the skills to achieve your stated goal?. Use the following scale as a guide.

0%	50%	100%
Not at all confident that I will achieve my goal	50-50 chance I will achieve my goal	Totally Confident I will Achieve my goal.

Write your confidence rating (from 0% - 100%) here: _____

Treatment Plan

Name: _John_   **Date:** _6/02/03_

GROUP: MOTIVATION GROUP

GOAL: To increase awareness of risks, level of self-efficacy and intrinsic desire for change.

Objective	Activity	Responsible Party	Frequency	Date Completed
A. Taking steps to reduce and/or no longer engage in your problem health behavior.	1. Self-reports last time engaged in problem health behavior.	Patient	1x/wk	
B. To assess stage of change, impact of problem health behavior and rate commitment and confidence levels to making changes in your behavior.	2. Attend orientation prior to entering motivation group. Complete all pre-assessment exercises.	Patient	1x	6/2/03
C. To increase awareness of risks of problem health behavior and level of self-efficacy to change.	3. Attend all four motivation group sessions. Complete all group exercises and homework assignments. Complete post-assessment exercises.	Patient	4x	
D. To reassess stages of change and level of impact of problem health behavior. To rate commitment and confidence levels to making changes in your behavior and what your next steps will be.	4. Contact referral provider after completing group.	Patient	1x	

John
Patient signature

6/2/03
Date

Provider signature

6/2/03
Date

Treatment Plan

Name: _____   **Date:** _____

GROUP: MOTIVATION GROUP
GOAL: To increase awareness of risks, level of self-efficacy and intrinsic desire for change.

Objective	Activity	Responsible Party	Frequency	Date Completed
A. Taking steps to reduce and/or no longer engage in your problem health behavior.	1. Self-reports last time engaged in problem health behavior.	Patient	1x/wk	
B. To assess stage of change, impact of problem health behavior and rate commitment and confidence levels to making changes in your behavior.	2. Attend orientation prior to entering motivation group. Complete all pre-assessment exercises.	Patient	1x	
C. To increase awareness of risks of problem health behavior and level of self-efficacy to change.	3. Attend all four motivation group sessions. Complete all group exercises and homework assignments. Complete post-assessment exercises.	Patient	4x	
D. To reassess stages of change and level of impact of problem health behavior. To rate commitment and confidence levels to making changes in your behavior and what your next steps will be.	4. Contact referral provider after completing group.	Patient	1x	

_____
Patient signature

_____
Date

_____
Provider signature

_____
Date

Group Summary (Patient Weekly Update)

GROUP: Motivation Group

Facilitator: _____   **Date:** _6/02/03_____

Patient's Name: _John_____   **Group Time:** _90 minutes_____

Right now I'm feeling: *Nervous*

The topic of group today was: *Orientation, stages of change*

What I learned about myself in this session: *That it is normal to feel two ways about change.*

How I'm feeling about group now: *Looking forward to learning more.*

Facilitator Notes:

Facilitator Signature: _____   Date: _____

SESSION TWO: Feelings
Time Allowed: 90 minutes

Rationale for this session
This session is designed to provide the opportunity to normalize reactance Brehm's Theory (1981) states that when behavioral freedom and autonomy are threatened, the probability and perceived desirability of the to-be-lost behavior will increase.

Purpose
This session helps move patients away from external requirements toward intrinsic desires for change. They need to vent their feelings about being required or pressured to make changes. Also they may acknowledge feelings (e.g. relief or worry) that suggest intrinsic awareness of their need for change. The process allows patients to begin to clarify need for change and articulate the feelings related to change.

The second exercise provides the opportunity to clarify feelings related to the areas of their lives they identified as impacted by their problem health behavior in Session One. This adds another layer to the awareness for change and begins to evoke change talk.

Facilitator Mind Set
The facilitator engages patients by utilizing an empathetic style of reflective listening, accurate understanding, acceptance and respect. Roll with resistance. Trust the process (one doesn't need to push it). The exercises elicit change talk. Listen for and affirm change talk. Let patients hear themselves. Know when to be quiet. Don't debate, argue or confront. Remember reactance is normal. Patients need to present their own arguments for change.

Materials needed for this session
Supplies: folders, pens, clipboards, dry erase board and dry erase pen.

Patient Handouts:
> Feelings – **Exercise 1& 2.** For **Exercise 2**, patients will need **Handout 5–** Areas of Impact; the self-assessment that they completed in the Orientation session, located in their folder.
> Group Summary

Other Paperwork:
>Patient Sign In sheet
>Roster/tracking sheet
>Vision homework:- for patients completing their third group session.
>**Post Assessment Handouts 16-18** and **Patient Satisfaction Survey Handout 19**, for patients presenting their Vision in this group.
>**Handouts 21** (Quotes) & **22** (Poem), for patients who are completing the Motivation Group.

Procedures

1.   Patients sign in and the facilitator checks the roster. (Sign in sheet and Rosters, **pg. 94-95).**

2.   The process for the check in is as follows: Name. Date of last time they engaged in their problem health behavior. Why they are in the group. Identify other groups they may be attending and the providers they see. Identify how they are feeling and how they are taking care of themselves. Check in with them to verify if they have done their homework. Notify those who are going to receive their vision homework to stay after group. Check in with the members who are completing the group to see if they have done their Vision Homework.

     If they have not completed their Vision homework, they will do the Vision exercise **(Handout 20, pg. 97-98)** in the final group session as part of their exercise. They will stay after group to complete the **Post-Assessment** exercises and compare their Pre and Post Assessment exercises with the facilitator. (Their **Pre Assessment exercises Handouts 5- 7**, are in their folders). Once they have completed their final group, the facilitator will disperse **Handouts 21-** Quotes and **22 -** Poem, **(pg. 85-86)**. These two handouts are given as a form of closure and to say good-bye to each patient.

3.   Put the quote on the board. Ask them to reflect on the quote that is about change. Ask how they relate to the quote in terms of changes they have made in their life, now or in their past.

4.   Review homework.

5.   Distribute the **Post Assessment** exercises and **Patient Satisfaction Survey** to those presenting their vision and completing their final group. The **Post**

Assessment exercises are **Handouts 16-18** and **Patient Satisfaction Survey**, **Handout 19**. All the handouts are to be completed in the group session.

6. Distribute the make-up exercise to the patients who have already completed this group exercise in a prior group session.

7. Distribute for this session, **Handout 9 – Feelings Exercise 1 & 2 (p.39 and p.40).** Instruct them to do the Feelings Exercise 1. The facilitator will read the directions on the handout to the group. As the patients are working on first exercise, the facilitator will explain the directions for the make-up exercises to the other patients.

8. Facilitating **Feelings Exercise 2**. The facilitator will have the patients retrieve the "Areas of Impact" exercise, they completed at Orientation **(Handout 5)** from their folder. The next step is to have them focus on (Part B) where they have prioritized and listed the areas of their lives impacted by their problem health behavior. The task is to have them identify feelings related to each of the identified areas. Discussion of feelings will follow once all patients have completed the exercise.

9. The Group Process: The facilitator will have each member read out loud both the feeling words they underlined and their paragraph from **Feelings Exercise 1.**

10. In the **Feelings Exercise 2**, the facilitator will explain to the patients that this exercise may bring up vulnerable feelings. It is important for everyone to trust the process and to let them hear themselves say out loud what they have written. Allow them time to describe their feelings related to the areas of their lives impacted by their problem health behavior. If patients can only articulate a simple association (ex. Family: angry) that is "OK". Thank each person as they finish and move to the next individual. Once all the patients have had the opportunity to express themselves, let the session end. This allows them to experience the process. (Don't add something to fill time).

11. Have the patients doing make-up exercise present their work in the group session.

12. Have the members who are completing their final session, present their vision. Have them read their summary page and then their vision.

13. Have all the patients turn in their exercises. The patients will fill out the **Group Summary Sheet (pg.96)** while the facilitator makes copies of their exercises. The facilitator will return the original exercises back to the patients. Have the members put the originals back into the folders. The facilitator will collect the group summaries and folders as they leave.

14. The facilitator reviews the **Pre and Post Assessment** exercises with those patients who are completing their final session. The Pre-assessment exercises are in their folders. When a patient completes their final session, they will receive their folder and a copy of the **Quotes (Handout 21)** and the **Poem (Handout 22).**

15. The patients that need to complete the Vision Homework **(Handout 20, pg. 97-98)** will remain after the group session to review the exercise with the facilitator. The patients will take out three exercises they have completed from their folder: **Areas of Impact** – (Part B), **Feelings** underlined, and the six **Values** they prioritized. From the exercises, the patients will complete the vision exercise summary sheet, **(pg 97).** The facilitator will review the direction under **Part B** of the Vision exercise for patients to complete at home.

Name: *John*   Date: _____

Exercise 1. Review the list of feelings below and underline all the feelings you remember having on the day you were required or pressured to change your problem health behavior. After underlining your feelings, please write a short paragraph, on the following page, describing those feelings.

Exercise 2. Take the orientation exercise, **Areas of Impact,** out of your folder. Review the list of feelings below and write the feelings you are currently having next to each of the areas of your life that you prioritized on (Part B).

FEELINGS

Vulnerable	*Mad*	*Worried*	Confused
Loss of Control	Sad	*Powerlessness*	
Empty	Fearful	Frustrated	Rage
Startled	Disappointed	Happy	Hopeless
Numb	Irritated	Shocked	Angry Jealous
Restless	Content	Belittled	Oppressed
Inadequate	Stunned	Tired	Jumpy *Guilty*
Outraged	Depressed	Satisfied	Invisible
Exhausted	Remorseful	Glad	*Embarrassed*
Relaxed	*Anxious*	Relief	*Nervous*

Name: _John_ _____   Date: _____

FEELINGS

Vulnerable- after not complying with my doctor's orders, I was afraid to make another appointment.

Worried-Had many concerns that this wouldn't be a change I could see myself achieving.

Mad- That once again I was finding myself backed in a corner, with no other options.

Powerlessness-Knew I had no choice in the matter.

Guilty-Because I didn't give myself a real chance to change before all this happened.

Embarrassed -Because I was told to make these changes several years ago.

Anxious- Know I should to get started.

Nervous- Because I know I am just one step away from disappointing everyone.

Name: _____   Date: _____

Exercise 1. Review the list of feelings below and underline all the feelings you remember having on the day you were required or pressured to change your problem health behavior. After underlining your feelings, please write a short paragraph, on the following page, describing those feelings.

Exercise 2. Take the orientation exercise, **Areas of Impact,** out of your folder. Review the list of feelings below and write the feelings you are currently having next to each of the areas of your life that you prioritized on (Part B).

FEELINGS

Vulnerable	Mad	Worried	Confused	
Loss of Control	Sad	Powerlessness		
Empty	Fearful	Frustrated	Rage	
Startled	Disappointed	Happy	Hopeless	
Numb	Irritated	Shocked	Angry	Jealous
Restless	Content	Belittled	Oppressed	
Inadequate	Stunned	Tired	Jumpy	Guilty
Outraged	Depressed	Satisfied	Invisible	
Exhausted	Remorseful	Glad	Embarrassed	
Relaxed	Anxious	Relief	Nervous	

Name: _____   Date: _____

FEELINGS

Exercise 2

Name: *John*   Date:_____

Areas of Impact Assessment (Part A)

On a scale of 1 - 4, with 1 being the *least* impacted, and 4 being the *most*, please circle the level of impact your problem health behavior has had on the different areas of your life.

Relationships	1	2	③	4
Work	1	②	3	4
Financial	1	②	3	4
Legal	1	②	3	4
Family	①	2	3	4
Education	1	②	3	4
Community	1	②	3	4
Physical Health	1	②	3	4
Emotional Health	1	2	③	4
Spirituality	①	2	3	4
Hobbies/Interests	1	2	③	4
Social Life	1	2	③	4
Character/Morals/Values	1	2	③	4
Self-esteem	1	②	3	4

(Part B) List the areas *most* impacted (3 or 4) by your problem health behavior, in order of importance.

1. *relationships—worried and disappointed*

2. *character, morals, values—empty*

3. *emotional health—sad, frustrated*

4. *hobbies, interests—worried and anxious*

5. *social life—nervous, confused, lonely*

6.

7.

SESSION THREE: Pro's and Cons
Time Allowed: 90 minutes

Rationale
Janis and Mann's decisional balance theory (1977) states that decision -making is a process of weighing cognitively the pros and cons of change.

Purpose of this Session
This session focuses on patient's ambivalence, the "good things" and "not so good things" about their problem health behavior. It serves to develop an awareness of risks by weighing the costs and benefits of one's problem health behavior. It also focuses on the patient's ability to assess their degree of self-efficacy to change. Emphasis is placed on the power of the short term "pros" and options to successfully alter or avoid engaging in the problem health behavior.

Facilitator Mind Set
Let the patient do the identification. Listen for their identification of problems associated with their problem health behavior (problem recognition). Affirm areas where the patient is demonstrating strength in identifying options to avoid or alter problem health behavior. Affirm the patient's recognition of additional areas of concern. The facilitator also provides a menu of options to assist patients in making additional choices. Allowing them to take ownership of their strengths to address areas of concern builds intrinsic motivation.

Materials needed for this session
Supplies: folders, pens, clipboards, dry erase board and dry erase pen.

Patient Handouts:
Individual exercise: Handouts - **10a & 10b,** for patients who missed the Group Brainstorming.
Short Term Pros
Altered States Descriptor
Homework: Menu of Alternatives & Altered States Categorizer

Other Paperwork:
Patient Sign In sheet
Roster/tracking sheet
Vision homework – if the patient will be completing his/her third group session.
Post Assessment Handouts – 16-18 and **Handout 19- Patient Satisfaction Survey** for the patients presenting their Vision in this group.
Handouts 21 (Quotes) & **22** (Poem), for patients who have completed the Motivation Group.

Procedures

1.   Patients sign in and the facilitator checks the roster. (Sign in sheet and Rosters, **pg. 94-95).**

2.   The process for the check in is as follows: Name. Date of last time they engaged in their problem health behavior. Why they are in the group. Identify other groups they may be attending and the providers they see. Identify how they are feeling and how they are taking care of themselves. Check in with them to verify if they have done their homework. Notify those who are going to receive their vision homework to stay after group. Check in with the members who are completing the group to see if they have done their Vision Homework.

     If they have not completed their Vision homework, they will do the Vision exercise **(Handout 20, pg. 97-98)** in the final group session as part of their exercise. They will stay after group to complete the **Post-Assessment** exercises and compare their Pre and Post Assessment exercises with the facilitator. (Their **Pre Assessment exercises Handouts 5-7**, are in their folders). Once they have completed the entire group, the facilitator will disperse **Handouts 21-** Quotes and **22** - Poem, (**pg. 85-86**). These two handouts are given as a form of closure and to say good-bye to each patient.

3.   Put the quote on the board. Ask them to reflect on the quote that is about change. Ask how they relate to the quote in terms of changes they have made in their life, now or in their past.

4.   Review homework.

5.   Distribute the **Post Assessment** exercises and **Patient Satisfaction Survey** to those presenting their vision and completing their final group. The **Post**

Assessment exercises are **Handouts 16-18** and **Survey, Handout19-Patient Satisfaction**. All the handouts are to be completed in the group session.

6.   Distribute the make-up exercise to patients who have already completed this group exercise in a prior group session.

7.   Introduce for this session, the **Pros & Cons Exercise**. Draw Short Term and Long Term Pros and Cons grid on the board. Brainstorm with the group the four areas of the grid (short and long term pro's and cons). Start the brainstorm with writing out the short term pros of their problem health behavior. (If a patient misses this session and has to make it up, give them a blank pros and cons grid **(Handout 10a, p.47)**. Also give them a copy of the brainstorm grid **(Handout 10b, p.48)** to assist them in completing their grid.

8.   **Handout 10 - Short term Pros Exercise (p.50).** Have the patients identify what their individual short-term pros are and answer questions 1-3. When patients completes the exercise have them read it out loud.

9.   Have some of patients take turns reading parts of **Handout 11- Alternative States Descriptor, (p.51).** Ask the patients what they thought it meant. Emphasize that when they are thinking of their own alternatives to their problem health behavior, to consider their body chemistry.

10.   Assign Homework: **Handout 12– Menu of Alternatives, (pg. 55-56).** Take the list of alternatives and mark the ones that they would be willing to do. With the items they have marked, use **Altered State Categorizer, (pg. 57)** to list the activities they selected, next to each of the following categories: physical, relaxation, cognitive, creative, meditation. On bottom half, list which of those activities they would be willing to engage in to help alter / avoid their problem health behavior.

11.   Remind them the homework will be reviewed the next week (bring it back).

12.   Have the patients doing make-up exercises present their work in the group session.

13.   Have the members who are completing their final session, present their vision. Have them read their summary page and then their vision.

14. Have all the patients turn in their exercises. The patients will fill out the **Group Summary** sheet (pg.96), while the facilitator makes copies of their exercises. The facilitator will return the original exercises back to the patients. Have the members put the originals back into the folders. The facilitator will collect the group summaries and folders as they leave.

15. The facilitator reviews the **Pre and Post Assessment** exercises with those patients who are completing their final session. The Pre-assessment exercises are in their folders. When a patient completes their final session, they will receive their folder and a copy of the **Quotes (Handout 21)** and the **Poem (Handout 22).**

16. The patients that need to complete the Vision Homework **(Handout 20 pg. 97-98)** will remain after the group session to review the exercise with the facilitator. The patients will take out three exercises they have completed from their folder: **Areas of Impact** – (Part B), **Feelings** underlined, and the six **Values** they prioritized. From the exercises, the patients will complete the vision exercise summary sheet, **(pg 97).** The facilitator will review the direction under **Part B** of the Vision exercise for patients to complete at home.

17. Facilitator copies brainstorming chart from the board, types it out for next session.

Name: *John*   Date: _____

Write the short and long term pros and cons of your problem health behavior.

SHORT TERM   LONG TERM

PROS	PROS
Social *Acceptance* *Stress* *Energy* *Focus*	*None*
CONS	CONS
Financial *Trust* *Sick* *Self-esteem* *Worry* *Stress* *Family* *Treatment* *Lonely*	*Financial* *Isolation* *Emotional health* *Physical health* *Family* *Employment* *Relationship* *Despair* *Death*

Name: _____   **Date:** _____

Write the short and long term pros and cons of your problem health behavior.

SHORT TERM   LONG TERM

PROS	PROS
CONS	CONS

Group Brainstorm

Write the short and long term pros and cons of your problem health behavior.

SHORT TERM   ## LONG TERM

PROS Multi-tasked Enjoyment Filled a void Social Forget about things Blocks out the world Acceptance Increases Confidence Image Relax Heighten Emotions Dulls Emotions Stress Energy Appetite Focus	**PROS** None

CONS
LOSSES:
  Money
  Energy
  Health-physical, mental
  Employment
  Relationships
  Family
  Freedom
  Reliability
  Dependability
  Trust
  Credibility
INCREASES:
  Anxiety
  Procrastination
  Depression
  Treatment
  Hermit Lifestyle
  Low Self-Esteem
  Anger
	CONS
	
	Isolation
	Despair
	Hospitalized
	Homeless
	Divorce
	Financial Losses
	Bankruptcy
	Family/children
	Unemployability
	Standing in Community
	Death

Short Term Pros

Name: _John_   Date: _____

1. **LIST THE SHORT TERM PROS THAT YOU ARE SUCCESSFULLY ALTERING OR AVOIDING.**

    Energy
    Focus

2. **LIST WHAT ACTIVITIES OR BEHAVIORS YOU ARE CURRENTLY DOING TO HELP YOU ALTER OR AVOID YOUR SHORT-TERM PROS.**

    Exercise
    Eat a balanced meal
    Keep a schedule
    Write out all appointments
    Plan my day

3. **LIST THE SHORT TERM PROS THAT YOU STILL FIND DIFFICULT TO ALTER AND / OR AVOID.**

    Social
    Acceptance
    Stress

Short Term Pros

Name: _____   Date: _____

1. LIST THE SHORT TERM PROS THAT YOU ARE SUCCESSFULLY ALTERING
   OR AVOIDING.

2. LIST WHAT ACTIVITIES OR BEHAVIORS YOU ARE CURRENTLY DOING TO HELP YOU
   ALTER OR AVOID YOUR SHORT-TERM PROS.

3. LIST THE SHORT TERM PROS THAT YOU STILL FIND DIFFICULT TO ALTER AND / OR
   AVOID.

50

Altered States Descriptor

It is human to seek altered states to give life purpose, meaning and fulfillment. Brain chemistry permits transient ecstasy or pleasure. Sustained ecstasy is neurophysiologically impossible.

Addictions and compulsive behaviors defy natural brain functioning, fabricating a sense of pleasure usually for a longer period of time and/or more intensively than what our brains can produce under normal circumstances.

The "crash" we experience after an addictive / compulsive episode is, in part, due to our bodies and brains attempting to compensate for the overload.

Natural highs are compatible with our brain functions. This is one reason we continue to feel good and do not experience a "crash" after a natural pleasure or after utilizing a healthy coping skill.

We rely on three distinct types of experiences to achieve feelings of well-being: *relaxation, excitement/arousal, and fantasy.*

- *Relaxation* **includes any activity that slows the body and mind down, such as meditating, bird watching, gardening, church, reading, walking, etc.**

- *Excitement/arousal* **is the opposite. It includes anything that speeds the body and mind up, such as competitive sports, running, skydiving, water/snow skiing, etc.**

- *Fantasy* **is using your imagination, and/or getting physical sensations from watching others perform an activity, such as watching sports, watching movies, reading, etc.**

Different addictions and compulsive behaviors fit into the same categories:

- *Relaxation*: **alcohol, heroin, tranquilizers, Quaaludes, barbiturates, etc.**

- *Excitement/arousal:* **gambling, sexual addiction, cocaine, amphetamines, etc.**

- *Fantasy:* **LSD, peyote, psylicybin mushrooms, marijuana, etc.**

Menu of Alternatives

Name: *John* _____   Date: _____

(Check the activities/ behaviors that you would be interested in trying
to help you alter / avoid your short term pros):

✓   H.A.L.T. (Hungry –eat, Angry –do something physical, Lonely –call a friend, Tired – sleep, rest).
      Read information
      Review your exercises from group
✓   Go to a support meeting
      Meet new friends
      Focus on doing a good job
✓   Do something to please family or friends
      Share your opinion and feelings
      Participate in lively discussions
✓   Complete a task
      Go people watching
      Express your affection
      Have coffee with a friend
      Anticipate a future event
      Go sun bathing / tanning
      Play with animals
✓   Plan a special project
      Learn a new skill
✓   Acquire knowledge
      Have a good night sleep
      Have time to do something you like
      Talk and listen to your loved ones
      Feel relaxed
✓   Be with a loved one
      Do something to make you feel attractive
      Breath fresh air
      Have pleasant thoughts about loved ones or friends
      Have sex
      Go out for lunch or dinner
      See or make good things happen to your family
      Pay someone a compliment
      Drive with care and caution
      Express yourself clearly
✓   Eat a good and special meal
      Wear something special
✓   Experience peace and quiet
      Laugh
      See beautiful things

Teach / coach / mentor
Participate in strenuous activities
Go to a play or concert
Contribute your time
Camp in the mountains
✓ Go fishing or hiking
Do volunteer work
✓ Ride a bus / train –go somewhere different
Buy something for yourself
Work on a problem
Assert yourself
Be at a special ceremony
Dine with friends
Participate in a church activity
✓ Make something from different materials
Dance
Go places where there are happy people
Listen to beautiful sounds of nature (wind, waterfall, waves)
Go on a date
Compete in a sports event
Give a present
Write a letter
Bath or take a shower
Attend a meeting or lecture
Attend a cultural activity
Cook a special meal
Receive advice from a mentor or friend
Take pictures or photographs
Look for interesting things (rocks, driftwood)
✓ Watch a sunset / sunrise / cloud formation
Invite friends to visit
Hear a funny story or joke
✓ Watch a video
Join and participate in a club
Go swimming
Play an outdoor game
✓ Listen to music
Read something special / go to the library
Use the computer
Watch a fire
Take a tour
Bake

Other Activities / Behaviors: *Sing, play golf, garden, bird-watching, keep a schedule, plan my day and paint.*

Altered States Categorizer

Name: *John* _____   Date: _____

(List the activities / behaviors you selected from the preceding 2 pages next to the appropriate category listed below):

⬤ **PHYSICAL ACTIVITIES:** *go for walks, play golf, garden, stretch.*

⬤ **RELAXATION ACTIVITIES:** *Plan a special project, be with a loved one, eat a special meal, ride a bus, make something, go fishing, watch a video, and listen to music.*

⬤ **COGNITIVE / AFFIRMATIONS:** *Go to a support meeting, do something to please family or friends, and acquire knowledge, keep a schedule and plan my day.*

⬤ **ART / CREATIVE / AESTHETIC:** *Watch a sunrise or sunset, bird-watching, paint.*

⬤ **MEDITATION / PRAYER:** *Experience peace and quiet, pray, go to church, sing.*

LIST BELOW THE ACTIVITIES / BEHAVIORS YOU WOULD BE WILLING TO ENGAGE IN TO HELP YOU ALTER / AVOID YOUR SHORT TERM PROS:

Play golf, ride a bus, go fishing, go for a walk, plan a special project, watch a video, listen to music, sing, go to church, keep a schedule, plan my day, and go to a support meeting.

Menu of Alternatives

Name: _____   Date: _____

(Check the activities / behaviors that you would be interested in trying to help you alter/avoid your short term pros):

H.A.L.T. (Hungry –eat, Angry –do something physical, Lonely –call a friend, Tired –sleep, rest).
Read information
Review your exercises from group
Go to a support meeting
Meet new friends
Focus on doing a good job
Do something to please family or friends
Share your opinion and feelings
Participate in lively discussions
Complete a task
Go people watching
Express your affection
Have coffee with a friend
Anticipate a future event
Go sun bathing / tanning
Play with animals
Plan a special project
Learn a new skill
Acquire knowledge
Have a good night sleep
Have time to do something you like
Talk and listen to your loved ones
Feel relaxed
Be with a loved one
Do something to make you feel attractive
Breath fresh air
Have pleasant thoughts about loved ones or friends
Have sex
Go out for lunch or dinner
See or make good things happen to your family
Pay someone a compliment
Drive with care and caution
Express yourself clearly
Eat a good and special meal
Wear something special
Experience peace and quiet
Laugh
See beautiful things

Teach / coach / mentor
Participate in strenuous activities
Go to a play or concert
Contribute your time
Camp in the mountains
Go fishing or hiking
Do volunteer work
Ride a bus / train –go somewhere different
Buy something for yourself
Work on a problem
Assert yourself
Be at a special ceremony
Dine with friends
Participate in a church activity
Make something from different materials
Dance
Go places where there are happy people
Listen to beautiful sounds of nature (wind, waterfall, waves)
Go on a date
Compete in a sports event
Give a present
Write a letter
Bath or take a shower
Attend a meeting or lecture
Attend a cultural activity
Cook a special meal
Receive advice from a mentor or friend
Take pictures or photographs
Look for interesting things (rocks, driftwood)
Watch a sunset / sunrise / cloud formation
Invite friends to visit
Hear a funny story or joke
Watch a video
Join and participate in a club
Go swimming
Play an outdoor game
Listen to music
Read something special / go to the library
Use the computer
Watch a fire
Take a tour
Bake
Other Activities / Behaviors:

_____
_____
_____
_____

Altered States Categorizer

Name: _____   Date: _____

(List the activities / behaviors you selected from the preceding 2 pages next to the appropriate category listed below):

PHYSICAL ACTIVITIES:

RELAXATION ACTIVITIES:

COGNITIVE / AFFIRMATIONS:

ART / CREATIVE / AESTHETIC:

MEDITATION / PRAYER:

LIST BELOW THE ACTIVITIES / BEHAVIORS YOU WOULD BE WILLING TO ENGAGE IN TO HELP YOU ALTER / AVOID YOUR SHORT-TERM PROS:

SESSION FOUR: Values
Time Allowed: 90 minutes

Rationale
"The further in the shift occurs, the more sweeping will be the resulting change." This is based on Rokeach's Values model (1973), <u>The Nature of Human Values.</u> Values are those elements from within one's self that are really important and have a preference focus. Values are standards and qualities that help establish a purpose and direction. When one identifies values, one has the power to exert considerable force, influencing and directing one's behavior. One gains insight about their decision-making processes. Decisions that are consistent with one's values provide a sense of satisfaction, enhanced energy and self-esteem. Values help determine one's philosophy and act as guidelines to determine the quality of one's life.

"To trigger change, one would seek to increase the discrepancy between status and goal, where I see myself being and where I want to be." This is based on Kanfer's (1986) Self Regulation Theory.

Purpose
Clarify, identify and affirm the patient values. Build intrinsic desire for change. Increase the patient's awareness of the discrepancy between problem health behavior and values. Heighten problem recognition and the desire for change, increase the patient's own arguments for change.

Facilitator Mind Set
The facilitator engages patients by utilizing an empathetic style of reflective listening, accurate understanding, acceptance and respect. Keep it safe; everything you do is purposeful to enhance motivation and commitment. Roll with resistance. Ambivalence is normal. Remember, every person's change process is an individual process and occurs at his/her own pace. Trust the process (don't need to push it). The exercises will elicit change talk. Listen to and affirm change talk. Let patients hear themselves. Know when to be quiet. Don't debate, argue or confront. Confrontation is a goal, not a strategy. "Patients will come face to face with a difficult reality in a way that will change them" (Miller).

Materials needed for this session
Supplies: folders, pens, clipboards, dry erase board and dry erase pen.

Patient Handouts:
> Values Exercises Instructions (1 & 2)
> List of Values
> Prioritized Values - Worksheet
> Homework – Exercise 2

Other Paperwork:
> Patient Sign In sheet
> Roster/tracking sheet
> Vision homework – if patient will be completing his/her third session.
> **Post Assessment Handouts – 16-18 and Handout 19 Patient Satisfaction Survey** for patients presenting their Vision in group.
> **Handouts 21** (Quotes) & **22** (Poem), for patients who have completed the Motivation Group.

Procedures

1. Patients sign in and the facilitator checks the roster. (Sign in sheet and Rosters, **pg. 94-95).**

2. The process for the check in is as follows: Check in. Name. Date of last time they engaged in their problem health behavior. Why they are in the group. Identify other groups they may be attending and the providers they see. Identify how they are feeling and how they are taking care of themselves. Check in with them to verify if they have done their homework. Notify those who are going to receive their vision homework to stay after group. Check in with the members who are completing the group to see if they have done their Vision Homework.

   If they have not completed their Vision homework, they will do the Vision exercise **(Handout 20, pg.97-98)** in the final group session as part of their exercise. They will stay after group to complete the **Post-Assessment** exercises and compare their Pre and Post Assessment exercises with the facilitator. (Their **Pre Assessment exercises Handouts 5-7**, are in their folders). Once they have completed the entire group, the facilitator will disperse **Handouts 21-** Quotes and **22** - Poem, **(pg. 85-86)**. These two handouts are given as a form of closure and to say good-bye to each patient.

3. Put the quote on the board. Ask them to reflect on the quote that is about change. Ask how they relate to the quote in terms of changes they have made in their life, now or in their past.

4. Review homework.

5. Distribute the **Post Assessment** exercises and **Patient Satisfaction Survey** to those presenting their vision and completing their final group. The **Post Assessment** exercises are **Handouts 16-18** and **Handout 19, Patient Satisfaction Survey**. All the handouts are to be completed in the group session.

6. Distribute the make-up exercise to patients who have already completed this group exercise in a prior group session.

7. The facilitator will start the session by having a short discussion on values, starting with the question "What are values"? Summarize the patient input. The facilitator will emphasize: that values are neither right nor wrong; values change over time; there are core values we learn growing up; values we adopt throughout our life experiences; and values that we still want to achieve.

    The facilitator will discuss the concept of discrepancies between values and behavior. Utilizing the following example, the facilitator demonstrates this. Example***: A person is offered a job that requires frequent travel. The person decides to accept the job without considering their number 1 value of family. Ask how this person might feel as a result of this decision?*** The discrepancy is the struggle between one's value and one's decision. What would make the decision congruent for this person?

8. The facilitator will introduce the values exercise, reminding the patients that the exercise may produce vulnerable feelings. To insure safety, there will not be any cross talk or debate about what individuals present. They will be asked to read their exercise out loud. The facilitator will inform them that they will be asked two questions when they have completed their presentation of their values exercise. The facilitator will also inform them that they may experience some discomfort in answering the questions. The facilitator will talk about "this discomfort" (discrepancy), after everyone has presented their exercise.

9. Give patients handout packet
   Values Exercise Instructions: Handout 13 - (pg. 63).
   Values Exercise 1 - Handout 14 - List of Values (pg. 66 & p.67)
   Prioritized Values Worksheet - Handout 14 (pg.69).

10. The facilitator will explain that this exercise is a four-step process. The patients will begin by reviewing the two-page list of values and they will check off all the values that are most important to them. When they have completed the first step, they will star their top six values. The third step is to have them prioritize the top six values they have selected.

11. The fourth step is to use the worksheet to list the six prioritized values. On the bottom half of the worksheet, the patients will define their values. The facilitator will explain that the definitions are very important because they emphasize the specific meaning for each individual. Although values may be similar, how people define them is what makes them unique.

12. The facilitator will explain to the patients to read out loud their six prioritized values and definitions, with no discussion. The facilitator will remind the patients that they will be asked two questions after they present their exercise. The facilitator will ask the following questions: 1) *How has your problem health behavior impacted each of your values?* **And 2)** *Which of your values support your problem health behavior? The facilitator will instruct them to respond to the questions by examining each of their values and definitions individually* (e.g. patients can't say "all of them").

13. The facilitator will thank each patient, when they finish reading their values **AND** after they respond to questions posed.

14. The facilitator will acknowledge that the patients may have felt some discomfort when describing the impact their problem health behavior has had on their values. This discomfort occurs when their problem health behavior is not congruent with their values. This is **discrepancy**.

15. The facilitator explains that when one's behaviors are congruent with their values they often describe feelings of inner peace.

16. **Homework Handout 15 - Values Exercise 2 (p.71).** The facilitator will have them write their top six values on the homework sheet. The patients

will be asked to keep their values in mind throughout the next week. This exercise is designed to emphasize the potential changes in patient's problem health behaviors as they integrate their values into their daily lives.

17. Remind them the homework will be reviewed the next week (bring it back).

18. Have the patients doing make-up exercise present their work in the group session.

19. Have the members who are completing their final session, present their vision. Have them read their summary page and then their vision.

20. Have all the patients turn in their exercises. The patients will fill out the **Group Summary** sheet (pg.96), while the facilitator makes copies of their exercises. The facilitator will return the original exercises back to the patients. Have the members put the originals back into the folders. The facilitator will collect the group summaries and folders as they leave.

21. The facilitator reviews the **Pre and Post Assessment** exercises with those patients who are completing their final session. The Pre-assessment exercises are in their folders. When a patient completes their final session, they will receive their folder and a copy of the **Quotes (Handout 21)** and the **Poem (Handout22).**

22. The patients that need to complete the Vision Homework **(Handout 20 (pg. 97-98)** will remain after the group session to review the exercise with the facilitator. The patients will take out three exercises they have completed from their folder: **Areas of Impact** – (Part B), **Feelings** underlined, and the six **Values** they prioritized. From the exercises, the patients will complete the vision exercise summary sheet, **(pg 97).** The facilitator will review the direction under **Part B** of the Vision exercise for patients to complete at home.

Name: _____   Date: _____

VALUES EXERCISES INSTRUCTIONS

GROUP EXERCISE 1: Read through the two-page list of values and check off your most important values. From the values that you selected, star the top six. Now prioritize them, numbering your values one through six. On the worksheet, list your prioritized top six values, and define them.

HOMEWORK:

EXERCISE 2: List your six prioritized values and write any behaviors and/or activities you engaged in during the week, that support your values.

Exercise 1

List of Values

	✓	ACCEPTANCE	to fit in with others
		ACCURACY	to be correct in my opinions and actions
✳	✓	ACHIEVEMENT	to accomplish and achieve
		ADVENTURE	to have new and exciting experiences
		ATTRACTIVENESS	to be physically attractive
		AUTHORITY	to be in charge of others
		BEAUTY	to appreciate beauty around me
		CARING	to take care of others
		COMFORT	to have a pleasant, enjoyable life
	✓	COMPASSION	to feel concern for others
		COMPLEXITY	to have a life full of variety and change
✳	✓	CONTRIBUTION	to make a contribution that will endure
		COURTESY	to be polite and considerate to others
		CREATIVITY	to have new and original ideas
✳	✓	DEPENDABILITY	to be reliable and trustworthy
		ECOLOGY	to live in harmony with the environment
✳	✓	FAITHFULNESS	to be loyal and reliable in relationships
		FAME	to be known and recognized
	✓	FAMILY	to have a happy, loving family
		FLEXIBILITY	to adjust to new or unusual situations easily
		FORGIVENESS	to be forgiving of others
		FRIENDS	to have close, supportive friends
		FUN	to play and have fun
	✓	GENEROSITY	to give what I have to others
		GOD'S WILL	to seek and obey the will of God
	✓	GROWTH	to keep changing and growing
		HEALTH	to be physically well and healthy
		HELPFULNESS	to be helpful to others
		HONESTY	to be truthful and genuine
		HOPE	to maintain a positive and optimistic outlook
	✓	HUMILITY	to be modest and unassuming
		HUMOR	to see the humorous side of myself
	✓	INDEPENDENCE	to be free from dependence on others
		INDUSTRY	to work hard and well at my life tasks
		INNER PEACE	to experience personal peace
		INTIMACY	to share my innermost feelings with others
		JUSTICE	to promote equal and fair treatment for all

		KNOWLEDGE	to learn and possess valuable knowledge
	✓	LEISURE	to take time to relax and enjoy
		LOGIC	to live rationally and sensibly
		LOVED	to be loved by those close to me
		MODERATION	to avoid excesses and find a middle ground
	✓	MONOGAMY	to have one close, loving relationship
		ORDERLINESS	to have a life that is ordered and organized
		PLEASURE	to feel good
		POPULARITY	to be well-liked by many people
		POWER	to have control over others
	✓	RESPONSIBILITY	to make and carry out important decisions
		REALISM	to see and act realistically and practically
		RISK	to take risks and chances
		ROMANCE	to have intense, exciting love relationships
		SAFETY	to be safe and secure
		SELF-CONTROL	to be disciplined and govern my own actions
		SELF-ESTEEM	to like myself just as I am
✳	✓	SELF-KNOWLEDGE	to have a honest understanding of myself
		SERVICE	to be of service to others
		SEXUALITY	to have an active and satisfying sex life
		SIMPLICITY	to live life simply, with minimal needs
	✓	STABILITY	to have a life that stays fairly consistent
		STRENGTH	to be physically strong
		SPIRITUALITY	to grow spiritually
	✓	TOLERANCE	to accept and respect those unlike myself
		TRADITION	to follow set patterns of the past
✳	✓	VIRTUE	to live a morally pure and excellent life
		WEALTH	to have plenty of money
		WORLD PEACE	to work to promote peace in the world

LIST OTHER VALUES YOU MAY HAVE NOT LISTED:

_____

_____

_____

Exercise 1

List of Values

ACCEPTANCE	to fit in with others
ACCURACY	to be correct in my opinions and actions
ACHIEVEMENT	to accomplish and achieve
ADVENTURE	to have new and exciting experiences
ATTRACTIVENESS	to be physically attractive
AUTHORITY	to be in charge of others
BEAUTY	to appreciate beauty around me
CARING	to take care of others
COMFORT	to have a pleasant, enjoyable life
COMPASSION	to feel concern for others
COMPLEXITY	to have a life full of variety and change
CONTRIBUTION	to make a contribution that will endure
COURTESY	to be polite and considerate to others
CREATIVITY	to have new and original ideas
DEPENDABILITY	to be reliable and trustworthy
ECOLOGY	to live in harmony with the environment
FAITHFULNESS	to be loyal and reliable in relationships
FAME	to be known and recognized
FAMILY	to have a happy, loving family
FLEXIBILITY	to adjust to new or unusual situations easily
FORGIVENESS	to be forgiving of others
FRIENDS	to have close, supportive friends
FUN	to play and have fun
GENEROSITY	to give what I have to others
GOD'S WILL	to seek and obey the will of God
GROWTH	to keep changing and growing
HEALTH	to be physically well and healthy
HELPFULNESS	to be helpful to others
HONESTY	to be truthful and genuine
HOPE	to maintain a positive and optimistic outlook
HUMILITY	to be modest and unassuming
HUMOR	to see the humorous side of myself and the world
INDEPENDENCE	to be free from dependence on others
INDUSTRY	to work hard and well at my life tasks
INNER PEACE	to experience personal peace
INTIMACY	to share my innermost feelings with others
JUSTICE	to promote equal and fair treatment for all

KNOWLEDGE	to learn and possess valuable knowledge
LEISURE	to take time to relax and enjoy
LOGIC	to live rationally and sensibly
LOVED	to be loved by those close to me
MODERATION	to avoid excesses and find a middle ground
MONOGAMY	to have one close, loving relationship
ORDERLINESS	to have a life that is well-ordered and organized
PLEASURE	to feel good
POPULARITY	to be well-liked by many people
POWER	to have control over others
RESPONSIBILITY	to make and carry out important decisions
REALISM	to see and act realistically and practically
RISK	to take risks and chances
ROMANCE	to have intense, exciting love relationships
SAFETY	to be safe and secure
SELF-CONTROL	to be disciplined and govern my own actions
SELF-ESTEEM	to like myself just as I am
SELF-KNOWLEDGE	to have a honest understanding of myself
SERVICE	to be of service to others
SEXUALITY	to have an active and satisfying sex life
SIMPLICITY	to live life simply, with minimal needs
STABILITY	to have a life that stays fairly consistent
STRENGTH	to be physically strong
SPIRITUALITY	to grow spiritually
TOLERANCE	to accept and respect those unlike myself
TRADITION	to follow set patterns of the past
VIRTUE	to live a morally pure and excellent life
WEALTH	to have plenty of money
WORLD PEACE	to work to promote peace in the world

LIST OTHER VALUES YOU MAY HAVE NOT LISTED:

_____

_____

_____

WORKSHEET

Name *John*   Date _____

HIGH PRIORITY VALUES

1. <u>*achievement*</u>

2. <u>*contribution*</u>

3. <u>*dependability*</u>

4. <u>*faithfulness*</u>

5. <u>*self-knowledge*</u>

6. <u>*virtue*</u>

DEFINE YOUR VALUES:

1. *To stick to my everyday planner, mental and on paper and complete anything that has to be completed.*

2. *To give my best to help anyone who may be interested in my opinion or need what I have to give.*

3. *When I say I'll be there I will. When I think I can do it, it will be done.*

4. *To be faithful in all my relationships. I have everything I need to be loyal and reliable.*

5. *I know myself better than anyone. To be honest and open and continue to grow.*

6. *My virtue is located deep inside my self-knowledge. Now all I need is the combination.*

WORKSHEET

Name _____   **Date** _____

HIGH PRIORITY VALUES

1._____

2. _____

3. _____

4. _____

5. _____

6. _____

DEFINE YOUR VALUES:

1. _____

_____

2._____

_____

3._____

_____

4._____

_____

5._____

_____

6._____

_____

HOMEWORK

Name *John*   Date _____

EXERCISE 2
List your six prioritized values and write any behaviors and/or activities you engaged in during the week, that support your values.

1. <u>*achievement*</u> *- Working on my projects at home.*

2. <u>*contribution*</u> *- Helping my neighbor move.*

3. <u>*dependability*</u> *- Going to group, work, meetings. Making all my appointments.*

4. <u>*faithfulness*</u> *- Being monogamous.*

5. <u>*self-knowledge*</u> *- Being honest with myself and my family.*

6. <u>*virtue*</u> *- Being aware of my values everyday.*

HOMEWORK

Name _John_   Date _____

EXERCISE 2

List your six prioritized values and write any behaviors and/or activities you engaged in during the week, that support your values.

1. _____

2. _____

3. _____

4. _____

5. _____

6. _____

SESSION FIVE: Vision/Post Assessment
Time Allowed: 90 minutes

Rationale for this session
Creating a vision comes out of understanding who you are. Rediscovering who you are motivates change and inspires a new vision. With a fuller understanding of yourself, you can develop a renewed sense of going after what you really want. Creating your vision has to do with helping you reconnect with your own potential. Having a vision motivates you to be genuinely interested in a different path and reclaiming parts of yourself that you thought were lost.

Purpose
To reassess patient's commitment, confidence levels and motivation for change. Patients will confront their own arguments for change and come to terms with any discrepancies of status and goal. The vision will evoke the patient's intentions to change and strengthen optimism that change is possible.

Facilitator Mind Set
The facilitator engages patients by utilizing an empathetic style of reflective listening, accurate understanding, acceptance and respect. Keep it safe; everything you do is purposeful to enhance motivation and commitment. Roll with resistance. Ambivalence is normal. Remember, every person's change process is an individual process and occurs at his/her own pace. Trust the process (don't need to push it). The exercises will elicit change talk. Listen to and affirm change talk. Let patients hear themselves. Know when to be quiet. Don't debate, argue or confront. Confrontation is a goal, not a strategy. "Patients will come face to face with a difficult reality in a way that will change them" (Miller).

Materials:
Vision handout if the patient didn't complete it at home.
Post-Assessment packet:
Areas of Impact
Wheel of Change
Commitment Rating
Patient Satisfaction Survey
Quotes and Poem

Other Paperwork
Patient Sign In sheet
Roster/tracking sheet
Vision homework: For patients completing their third group session.
Post Assessment Handouts 16-18 and Patient Satisfaction Survey Handout 19,
for patients presenting their Vision in this group.
Handouts 21 (Quotes) & 22 (Poem), for patients who are completing the
Motivation Group

Procedures

1. Patients sign in and the facilitator checks the roster. (Sign in sheet and Rosters, **pg. 94-95).**

2. The process for the check in is as follows: Check in. Name. Date of last time they engaged in their problem health behavior. Why they are in the group. Identify other groups they may be attending and the providers they see. Identify how they are feeling and how they are taking care of themselves. Check in with them to verify if they have done their homework. Notify those who are going to receive their vision homework to stay after group.

3. Put the quote on the board. Ask them to reflect on the quote that is about change. Ask how they relate to the quote in terms of changes they have made in their life, now or in their past.

4. Review homework.

5. Before starting the group exercise, give those patients presenting their visions, the Post assessment packet, which includes the **Handouts 16-19 Post Assessment Exercises and Patient Satisfaction Survey (p.79-82)** to be completed during the group session. After they complete this packet they will wait for the rest of the group to finish their exercise for this session.

6. Upon completion of the group exercise, those patients completing the motivation group will present their visions. The facilitator will ask them to read their summary page first and then their vision (Handout 20 - Example pg. 83-84).

7. Have all the patients turn in their exercises. The patients will fill out the **Group Summary** sheet (**pg.96**), while the facilitator makes copies of their exercises. The facilitator will return the original exercises back to the

patients. Have the members put the originals back into the folders. The facilitator will collect the group summaries and folders as they leave.

8. The facilitator reviews the **Pre and Post Assessment** exercises with those patients who have completed their final group session. The Pre-assessment exercises are in their folders. (**Facilitator Note:** When comparing the Pre and Post Assessment exercises you may observe the following on patient's Post Assessment exercises: (1) <u>Areas of Impact:</u> that the patient identified more areas of impact and rated the level of impact higher. (2) <u>Wheel of Change</u>: that the patient moved towards a different stage of change and (3) <u>Commitment and Confidence Level</u>: that the patient's commitment level may be higher and his/her confidence level may be lower. All these changes are related to the increase in patient's awareness of the need for change and his/her sense of self-efficacy that change is possible

9. When a patient has completed their final session, they will receive their folder and a copy of the **Quotes (Handout 21)** and the **Poem (Handout 22)** as a form of closure.

10. The patients that need to complete the Vision Homework **(Handout 20, pg. 97-98)** will remain after the group session to review the exercise with the facilitator. The patients will take out three exercises they have completed from their folder: **Areas of Impact** – (Part B), **Feelings** underlined, and the six **Values** they prioritized. From the exercises, the patients will complete the vision exercise summary sheet, (**pg 97**). The facilitator will review the direction under **Part B** of the Vision exercise for patients to complete at home.

11. The facilitator will complete the treatment plans of those patients who completed the motivation group (**Example Treatment Plan, pg. 87**).

Post Assessment Handouts (16-19)

Name: *John*   Date: _____

Areas of Impact Assessment

(Part A) On a scale of 1- 4, with 1 being the *least* impacted, and four being the *most*, please circle the level of impact your problem health behavior has had on the different areas of your life.

Relationships	1	2	3	④
Work	1	2	③	4
Financial	1	2	3	④
Legal	1	2	3	④
Family	1	②	3	4
Education	1	②	3	4
Community	1	②	3	4
Physical Health	1	2	③	4
Emotional Health	1	2	③	4
Spirituality	1	2	③	4
Hobbies/Interest	1	2	3	④
Social Life	1	2	③	4
Character/Morals/Values	1	②	3	4
Self-esteem	1	②	3	4

(Part B) List the areas most impacted (3 or 4) by your problem health behavior, in order of importance.

1. *relationships*

2. *financial*

3. *legal*

4. *hobbies / interests*

5. *work*

6. *physical health*

7. *social life*

8. *emotional health*

9. *spirituality*

Name: *John* _____   Date: _____

PROCHASKA-DICLEMENTE'S WHEEL OF CHANGE

Please read the definition of each stage of change, written below, and shade in the area of the wheel that identifies where you are, in the process of changing your problem health behavior.

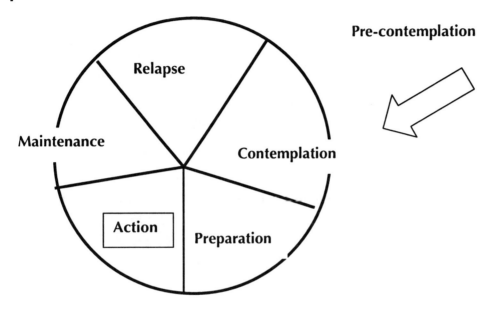

The Six Stages Of Change:

1. Pre-contemplation-**You do not think that your problem health behavior is a problem.**

2. Contemplation-**You are considering the possibility of changing your problem health behavior and at the same time rejecting the idea of change.**

3. Preparation-**You are leaning toward change, seriously considering no longer engaging in your problem health behavior.**

4. Action-**You are taking steps to no longer engage in your problem health behavior.**

5. Maintenance-**You are identifying and using strategies to prevent relapse and addressing other areas of your life.**

6. Relapse-**You are renewing the processes of contemplation, preparation and action and not giving up on your goal.**

Post-Assessment Exercise

Name: *John* _____   Date: _____

Self-Commitment Rating

At this moment, how important is it that you change your problem health behavior? How hard are you willing to work and how much are you willing to do, to achieve this goal? Answer this question by writing a number from 0-100 in the designated space below, using the following scale as a guide.

1	25	50	75	100
Not important at all	Less important than most other things I would like to achieve	About as important as most of the other things I would like to achieve	More important than most of the other things I would like to achieve	The most important thing in my life

Write your goal importance rating (from 0-100) here: __75%__

Self-Confidence Rating (Do I believe I can succeed?)

In the designated space below indicate how confident you feel that you have the skills to achieve your stated goal. Use the following scale as a guide.

0%	50%	100%
Not at all confident that I will achieve my goal	50-50 chance I will achieve my goal	Totally Confident I will Achieve my goal.

Write your confidence rating (from 0% - 100%) here: __100%__

Patient Satisfaction Survey

Patient: _John_____   Date:_____

1. HAVE YOU MOVED FORWARD, BACKWARD, OR STAYED THE SAME, REGARDING YOUR ASSESSMENT OF THE NEED TO CHANGE YOUR PROBLEM HEALTH BEHAVIOR, SINCE STARTING THIS GROUP. **(Please describe):**

   Due to the fact my attitude is much more positive, I have moved forward.

2. HOW USEFUL WERE THESE SELF – ASSESSMENT EXERCISES TO YOU? (In what way):

   They were put together very clearly. I feel much more comfort in explaining my deepest hard to find thoughts.

3. NAME TWO THINGS YOU LEARNED ABOUT YOURSELF?

   1. My inner strength is quite amazing.
   2. I don't have to please others to be me.

4. DID YOU FEEL UNDERSTOOD, LISTENED TOO AND RESPECTED BY THIS FACILITATOR? **And were your needs being addressed? (Please Describe)**

   Yes, I never felt looked down upon or talked down to. I'm clearer about the steps I know I need to take.

Post/Assessment Handouts (16-19)

Name: _____   Date: _____

Areas of Impact Assessment

(Part A) On a scale of 1- 4, with 1 being the *least* impacted, and four being the *most*, please circle the level of impact your problem health behavior has had on the different areas of your life.

Relationships	1	2	3	4
Work	1	2	3	4
Financial	1	2	3	4
Legal	1	2	3	4
Family	1	2	3	4
Education	1	2	3	4
Community	1	2	3	4
Physical Health	1	2	3	4
Emotional Health	1	2	3	4
Spirituality	1	2	3	4
Hobbies/Interest	1	2	3	4
Social Life	1	2	3	4
Character/Morals/Values	1	2	3	4
Self-esteem	1	2	3	4

(Part B) List the areas *most* impacted (3 or 4) by your problem health behavior, in order of importance.

1.

2.

3.

4.

5.

6.

7.

8.

Post–Assessment Exercise

Name_____   Date:_____

PROCHASKA-DICLEMENTE'S WHEEL OF CHANGE

Please read the definition of each stage of change, written below, and shade in the area of the wheel that identifies where you are, in the process of changing your problem health behavior.

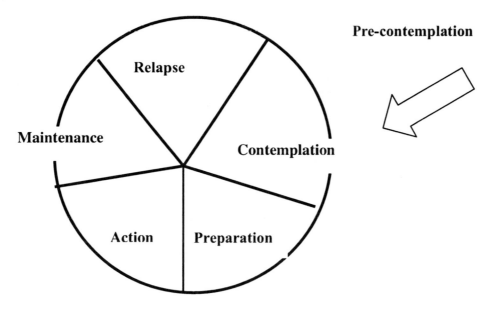

The Six Stages Of Change:

1. Pre-contemplation-**You do not think that your problem health behavior is a problem.**

2. Contemplation-**You are considering the possibility of changing your problem health behavior and at the same time rejecting the idea of change.**

3. Preparation-**You are leaning toward change, seriously considering no longer engaging in your problem health behavior.**

4. Action-**You are taking steps to no longer engage in your problem health behavior.**

5. Maintenance-**You are identifying and using strategies to prevent relapse and addressing other areas of your life.**

6. Relapse-**You are renewing the processes of contemplation, preparation and action and not giving up on your goal.**

Post–Assessment Exercise

Name: _____   Date: _____

Self-Commitment Rating

At this moment, how important is it that you change your problem health behavior? How hard are you willing to work and how much are you willing to do, to achieve this goal? Answer this question by writing a number from 0-100 in the designated space below, using the following scale as a guide.

1	25	50	75	100
Not important at all	Less important than most other things I would like to achieve	About as important as most of the other things I would like to achieve	More important than most of the other things I would like to achieve	The most important thing in my life

Write your goal importance rating (from 0-100) here: _____

Self-Confidence Rating (Do I believe I can succeed?)

In the designated space below indicate how confident you feel that you have the skills to achieve your stated goal. Use the following scale as a guide.

0%	50%	100%
Not at all confident that I will achieve my goal	50-50 chance I will achieve my goal	Totally Confident I will Achieve my goal.

Write your confidence rating (from 0% - 100%) here: _____

Patient Satisfaction Survey

Patient:_____   **Date:**_____

1. HAVE YOU MOVED FORWARD, BACKWARD, OR STAYED THE SAME, REGARDING YOUR ASSESSMENT OF THE NEED TO CHANGE YOUR PROBLEM HEALTH BEHAVIOR, SINCE STARTING THIS GROUP. **(Please describe):**

2. HOW USEFUL WERE THESE SELF – ASSESSMENT EXERCISES TO YOU? **(In what way?):**

3. NAME TWO THINGS YOU LEARNED ABOUT YOURSELF?

4. DID YOU FEEL UNDERSTOOD, LISTENED TOO AND RESPECTED BY THIS FACILITATOR? **And were your needs being addressed? (Please Describe)**

Vision Exercise Summary Page

You are now coming to the end of the Motivation Group. To make a bridge from this Motivation Group to your next step, you will create a vision of the improvements or changes you hope will occur in your life as a result of your commitment to and eventual achievement of your goal.

PART A. Please utilize the information from the exercises you have completed in group, and list the following information about yourself.

MOST IMPORTANT AREAS OF IMPACT:

Relationships
Character, morals and values
Emotional health
Hobbies / interests
Social life

FEELINGS DURING FIRST CONTACT:

vulnerable	*mad*	*guilty*
embarrassed	*worried*	*nervous*
powerlessness	*anxious*	

VALUES:

Achievement	*Contribution*
Dependability	*Faithfulness*
Self-knowledge	*Virtue*

PART B. On the following page, write several paragraphs describing the improvements or changes you are hoping to make over the next 3-6 months.

- Focus on the <u>Areas of Impact</u> you identified and prioritized, as being most impacted by your problem health behavior.
- Add to your paragraph how you will feel when you make those improvements.
- Describe which of your values will support those changes and improvements.
- Use your imagination and don't limit or edit yourself.

Name: _John_   Date: _____

VISION

Within the next few months I hope to reduce my drinking to never. I know myself and it is definitely going to be a challenge, given the fact that all my friends drink when we get together to play cards. I plan on talking to them and explain that I am going to need their help. I know that when I accomplish this goal, I will be so proud of myself, and feel better. But I will have to remind myself on a daily basis how long it has taken me to get here. And if I back track I will reach out to my friends and use what I have learned to continue to work on this goal. What's important to me is to not give up on my goal due to feelings of guilt or shame. What I learned, that I need to remember, is an occasional lapse is normal when you are trying to change a behavior. I think that the value of achievement will help me through this because the word means that I worked towards something and I have!

Quotes

"What we call the beginning is often the end,
And to make our end is to make a beginning.
The end is where we start from."

T. S. Eliot

"I have always known that at last I would take this road,
but yesterday I did not know it would be today."

Narihira

"I can discard that which is unfitting and keep that which proved fitting,
and invent something new for that which I discarded."

Virginia Satir

"One change already influences other parts,
that means we can start anywhere."

Virginia Satir

POTENTIAL

It is something we can see in others,

If we see.

It is something we can feel in others,

If we feel.

It is something we can touch in others,

If we touch.

It is something we all have,

An inside desire to be more.

An energy so powerful, so human

It propels our growth.

Before it is kinetic,

Before there is change,

Our potential needs to be realized.

If we realize.

Ann Fields

Completed Treatment Plan

Name: _John_   Date: 6/02/03

GROUP: MOTIVATION GROUP

GOAL: To increase awareness of risks, level of self-efficacy and intrinsic desire for change.

Objective	Activity	Responsible Party	Frequency	Date Completed
A. Taking steps to reduce and/or no longer engage in your problem health behavior.	1. Self-reports last time engaged in problem health behavior.	Patient	1x/wk	**6/30/03**
B. To assess stage of change, impact of problem health behavior and rate commitment and confidence levels to making changes in your behavior.	2. Attend orientation prior to entering motivation group. Complete all pre-assessment exercises.	Patient	1x	**6/2/03**
C. To increase awareness of risks of problem health behavior and level of self-efficacy to change.	3. Attend all four motivation group sessions. Complete all group exercises and homework assignments. Complete post-assessment exercises.	Patient	4x	**6/30/03**
D. To reassess stages of change and level of impact of problem health behavior. To rate commitment and confidence levels to making changes in your behavior and what your next steps will be.	4. Contact referral provider after completing group.	Patient	1x	**6/30/03**

John

Patient signature

6/2/03

Date

_____

Provider signature

6/2/03

Date

PROVIDER PREPARATION
AND ORGANIZATION

Be Organized.

This is a concrete way to track patients and the process of patients moving through the group exercises.

Group Roster:
> List new patient's names on to the roster.
> Attach new member's treatment plan at the back of the roster.
> Place the initial of the exercise completed, under the correct date, next to each patient's name. (O – orientation, P- pros & cons, V- values, F- feelings, VS - vision).
> Place a (/) for excused or (x) for no show, under the correct date, next to the patient's name who did not come to group.
> Write VS and Completed, under the correct date, next to the patient's names who presented their visions and completed the post-assessment exercises.

Provider Orientation Folder:
> Copies of the following Handouts:
>> Orientation Sign-In sheet.
>> Group Norms
>> Facilitator Philosophy (Labels and Reactance)
>> Freedom …
>> Purpose of Group
>> Pre-Assessment Handouts:
>>> Areas of Impact
>>> Stages of Change
>>> Self-Commitment rating and Confidence rating
>> Treatment Plan
>> Group Summary / Sign-Out
> Folders – for new patients

Provider Group Folder divided into three parts. The front part is used in group, the middle is used for group preparation and the end is for patient's completed work
> Front: utilized in group:
>> Quotes; to write on the board.
>> Group check-in format; to write on the board.
>> Patient's Sign-In sheet.
>> Group roster, with attached treatment plans.
>> Patient's exercises, for the day.
>> Patient's summary - Sign-Out sheet.
> Middle:
>> A colored paper labeled Originals.
>>> Keep one original copy, of all the exercises, behind this paper.
>>> This way the provider can easily find the exercises that need to be copied when he/she is preparing for the next group.

> End: Patients completed copies of the exercises.

Place six different colored pieces of paper in the back of your folder.
Label them with the names of each of the exercises;
Pros & Cons, Feelings, Values, Vision / Post assessment exercises, and
Orientation / Pre assessment exercises.

Under each of these labeled colored papers is where you keep the copies of
your patient's completed exercises. (The original completed exercises are kept
in the patient's folders).

These copies are kept until the patients have completed the motivation group
and received his/her folder.

Group Preparation:

Take a look at the roster to determine which exercise the majority of the group needs to
complete.
>Count the number of patients who will be doing the group exercise.
>Make the copies of the exercise needed for the next group.
>Flag the front copy of the exercises with a sticky labeled _____ group exercise.

Take a look at the roster to see which patient's need to do a make-up group exercise
due to an absence.
>Make a copy of that exercise and flag the front of it with a sticky labeled with
their name.

Take a look at the roster and see which patients have completed two exercises, do not
include O - orientation.
>These patients will be receiving their vision exercise as homework, in the next
group.
>Make copies of the vision exercise and flag them with a sticky labeled with their
names.

Take a look at the roster to see which patients have completed all three exercises (P, V,
F) and will be presenting their vision.
>Make copies of the Post-assessment exercises they need to complete in their
final group; and flag the copies with a sticky labeled with their names.

At a glance - Provider reminders: (*Example Roster Handout p.91*)

Flag the front of the group roster with the following:
- Label a sticky with the names of the patients receiving their vision homework.
- Label a sticky with the names of the patients presenting their vision.
- Label a sticky with individuals doing make-up exercises and the names of
their exercises.
- Label a sticky with the name of the group exercise.
- Label a sticky with the homework exercise to be reviewed or handed in to the
group provider.

GROUP ROSTER EXAMPLE

List Topics Here ↓

VISION HOMEWORK — CORY

VISION — STEVE

O = Orientation
F = Feeling
P = Pros and Cons
V = Values
VS = Vision/Post Assessment

PROS & CONS HOMEWORK

GROUP EXERCISE — VALUES

Name ↓ Date →	Orientation 6/2	Feelings 6/9	Pros&Cons 6/16	Values 6/23	Pros&Cons 6/30	Feelings 7/7	Values 7/14	Feelings 7/21	Pros&Cons 7/28	Values 8/4
John	O	F	P	V	VS					
Howard		O	P	V	F	/	VS			
Rebecca		O	X	V	P	/	F	VS		
Ruth			O	/	P	F	V	VS		
Theresa					O	F	V	/	X	
Dean					O	/	X			
Steve						O	V	F	P	
Cory						O	/	F	P	
Dan							O	F	/	
Jacen								O	P	

Absence/=excused x= no show

FORMS

GROUP ROSTER EXAMPLE

List Topics Here ↓

O= Orientation F = Feeling P = Pros and Cons V = Values VS = Vision/Post Assessment	Orientation	Feelings	Pros & Cons	Values	Pros & Cons	Feelings	Values	Feelings	Pros & Cons	Values														
Name ↓ Date ➡	6/2	6/9	6/16	6/23	6/30	7/7	7/14	7/21	7/28	8/4														
John	O	F	P	V	VS																			
Howard		O	P	V	F	/	VS																	
Rebecca		O	X	V	P	/	F	VS																
Ruth			O	/	P	F	V	VS																
Theresa					O	F	V	/	X															
Dean					O	/	X																	
Steve						O	V	F	P															
Cory						O	/	F	P															
Dan							O	F	/															
Jacen							O	P																

Absence/=excused x= no show

GROUP ROSTER

List Topics Here ↓

O= Orientation F=Feelings P= Pros and cons V= Values VS= Vision /post assessment																					
Date →																					
Name ↓																					

Absence/=excused   x= no show

Group Sign-In

Date_____   **Provider** _____

NAME	DATE LAST ENGAGED IN PROBLEM HEALTH BEHAVIOR	CURRENT MOOD

Group Summary (Patient Weekly Update)

GROUP: _____

Facilitator: _____   **Date:** _____

Patient's Name: _____   **Group Time:** _____

Right now I'm feeling:

The topic of group today was:

What I learned about myself in this session:

How I'm feeling about group now:

_____

Facilitator Notes:

Facilitator Signature: _____ Date: _____

HOMEWORK

Vision Exercise Summary Page

You are now coming to the end of the Motivation Group. To make a bridge from this Motivation Group to your next step, you will create a vision of the improvements or changes you hope will occur in your life as a result of your commitment to and eventual achievement of your goal.

PART A. Please utilize the information from the exercises you have completed in group, and list the following information about yourself.

MOST IMPORTANT AREAS OF IMPACT:

FEELINGS DURING FIRST CONTACT:

VALUES:

PART B. On the following page, write several paragraphs describing the improvements or changes you are hoping to make over the next 3-6 months.

- Focus on the <u>Areas of Impact</u> you identified and prioritized, as being most impacted by your problem health behavior.
- Add to your paragraph how you will feel when you make those improvements.
- Describe which of your values support those changes and improvements.
- Use your imagination and don't limit or edit yourself.

Name: _____   **Date:** _____

VISION

Bibliography

Bem, D.J. (1972) *Self-perception Theory*. In L. Berkowitz (Ed.), *Advances in experimental social psychology* (Vol. 6, pp. 1-62). New York: Academic Press.

Brehm, S. S., & Brehm, J. W. (1981) *Psychological Reactance: A theory of freedom and control*. New York: Academic Press.

DiClemente, C. C., & Prochaska, J. O. (1998). *Toward a comprehensive, transtheoretical model of change: Stages of change and addictive behaviors*. In W. R. Miller & N. Heather (Eds.) *Treating addictive behaviors* (2nd ed., pp.3-24) New York: Plenum Press.

Janis, I. L., & Mann, L. (1977) *Decision-making: A psychological analysis of conflict, choice, and commitment*. New York: Free Press.

Kanfer, F. H. (1986) *Implications of a self-regulation model of theory for treatment of addictive behaviors*. In W. R. Miller & N. Heather (Ed.), *Treating addictive behaviors* (pp. 29-47). New York: Plenum Press.

Miller, W. R. & Rollnick, S (1991) Motivational interviewing: *Preparing people to change addictive behaviors*. New York: Guilford Press.

Rogers, R. W. & Mewborn, C. R. (1976) Fear appeals and attitude change: Effects of a threat's noxiousness, probability of occurrence, and the efficacy of coping responses. *Journal of Personality & Social Psychology*, 34, 54-61.

Rokeach, M (Ed.). (1979) *Understanding human values*. New York: Macmillan.

About the Author

Ann E. Fields, MSE., CADC 111, CGAC 11
Trainer/Consultant

Ann Fields is originally from Dover, New Jersey. She currently resides in Vancouver, Washington. Ms. Fields holds a Bachelor of Arts degree in Psychology from Catawba College, Salisbury, North Carolina, a Bachelor of Science in Behavior Technology from the University of North Carolina, Greensboro, North Carolina and a Masters of Education degree from Western Oregon University, Monmouth, Or. Ms. Fields also has master-level certifications in substance abuse and gambling addictions.

She has also worked with William Miller in the original training cohort and was selected to participate in the first "Training for Trainers" program established by Miller in 1993. Ms. Fields is a registered MINT trainer (Motivational Interviewing Network of Trainers) in Washington and Oregon.

She has worked in the counseling field for more than 25 years and specializes in behavioral change. Throughout her career, she has been involved with innovative programs utilizing behaviorally oriented, research-based strategies and techniques to effect change with individuals, families, service providers, communities and large systems.

Ms. Fields provides specialized training and consultation to professional practitioners in a variety of practice arenas such as: mental health, medical social work, substance abuse, gambling addictions, child welfare, juvenile justice, corrections, family violence and family preservation services. As a guest lecturer for the Graduate School of Social Work, Portland State University, she has provided social work students with a foundation of basic concepts for utilizing motivational interviewing in their beginning social work practice, since 1998. She is also a trainer for Daystar Education Associates and Portland State University's Continuing Education Program, both located in Portland, Oregon and is a national trainer for PESI HealthCare.

Made in the USA